Barbara Godfrey made journalism her career after graduating at Oxford in Modern Languages. In 1953 she and a friend spent a year as au pairs in a large house near Oslo, where her knowledge of German helped in mastering the Norwegian language. Her eldest son Christopher is also a "Norwegiophile" and speaks the language fluently.

After her spell "in service", which was the subject of a talk she gave on the BBC's *Woman's Hour,* she worked as a reporter on several Surrey newspapers. She then helped her late husband Robert, a former Fleet Street journalist, to launch the *Hayling Islander* newspaper, which won an award for editorial excellence and which is now owned by the *Portsmouth News.*

After five years living on the edge of Dartmoor, the couple moved to the tiny Channel Island of Alderney, where they founded the *Alderney Magazine.*

Barbara Godfrey, who still lives on Alderney, has also published short stories and a book of poetry, illustrated with her own hand-coloured drawings. Her watercolour and oil paintings of local scenes are on view in the island's art gallery.

NAUGHTY IN NORWAY

A Saucy Saga of the North

by
Barbara Godfrey

To Ole Nordmann with his roving blue eyes: *Skål!*

Published by

Black Cat Communications

High Ways
Les Mouriaux
Alderney
Channel Islands GY9 3UX
Great Britain

books@blackcatcommunications.co.uk

Naughty in Norway by Barbara Godfrey

First published 1999

ISBN 1 902976 00 2

Typeset in 11pt Sabon

Typesetting, layout & design by CRG Design & Black Cat Communications

BC23

Printed & bound by The Guernsey Press

The characters in this book are not intended to be those of any living persons

Contents

Foreword

The year 1953 was momentous for Great Britain – and for Alicia and me.

For our country, the Coronation of Queen Elizabeth II was the highlight of the year. For us, it was our big adventure as Norwegian housemaids.

We did not miss out entirely on the Coronation, though. As television had not yet reached Norway we had to content ourselves with the radio commentaries and the cinema film shown in Oslo, where the ceremony created almost as much interest as back home – especially as the queen was the great-niece of Norway's King Haakon VII.

The other big event of the year, the conquest of Mount Everest, also hit the headlines in the mountain-loving nation where we were working and playing.

Before we left England to go into service abroad the liveliest topics of conversation were the inauguration of General Eisenhower as President of the USA; America's detonation of a hydrogen bomb in the Pacific a few months earlier; and the hanging of young Derek Bentley, which roused bitter controversy among the opponents and supporters of capital punishment.

On a more cheerful note, tea and sweet rationing and UK identity cards had been abolished; a new American pin-up, Marilyn Monroe, was beginning to turn men's heads the world over; the BBC's latest offering, the crazy *Goon Show*, was a raging success; and Agatha Christie's *The Mousetrap* – still going strong 40 years later – had opened in London with “a fair degree of success”.

In the technological field, the first four-engine delta-wing jet bomber, the magnificent Vulcan, had made its maiden flight the previous summer; 3D and CinemaScope had hit the movie screens; and 27-inch TV sets made their debut at London’s radio show at Olympia.

As for sex, yes, it did exist – but in a far less rampant form than the widespread promiscuity of later years. The scourge of AIDS was unknown, the Pill was not available, and women did not yet have the right to take the final decision on having an abortion.

Many young people confined their premarital sexual encounters to what was commonly known as “snogging” or “canoodling”. Those who “went the whole hog”, as it was quaintly called, “made love” rather than “had sex”. But the leap into bed by virtual strangers for a one-night stand was not the norm.

Even in naughty Norway, where men dallied with charming insouciance, it was considered shameful to have an illegitimate child . . .

1
A Toss of the Coin

I leant against the boat rails and watched Alicia languidly through narrowed eyes as she prepared to flip the coin. Could she be going to cheat somehow? I wondered idly. After all, the prize was a big fish – the captain of the Norwegian cargo ship which was to take us to Oslo to seek fame and fortune.

The other passengers were too busy to notice us as they waved and called last messages to friends on the quayside. This was rapidly growing smaller as the boat made its way out of port until the people on shore were no more than colourful dots against the impressive backdrop of Dover's white cliffs and mighty castle.

Alicia and I wasted no time getting down to the serious business of planning our entertainment for the next few days on the desolate wastes of the North Sea. When the five øre coin clattered to the deck and I was the winner, I silently scolded myself for doubting my friend's integrity.

We had agreed the loser should have the third mate, who had already taken our fancy as the best-looking member of the crew. So during the crossing to Oslo the captain – an arrogant, bull-necked man in his forties – would keep me from boredom and the mate, a blond young Viking, would be Alicia's consolation prize.

We put our plan into action immediately. We knew the captain would be an easy target – he had made this obvious from the moment he welcomed us on board with a lingering squeeze of the hand and a surreptitious pat on our bottoms. The mate was a less easy proposition as he was forbidden access to the passenger quarters. He did, however, briefly cross the passenger deck on his way up to the bridge when it was his turn on watch.

Alicia laid her trap that morning when the unsuspecting mate made his way to the bridge. Seeing her hunting for a small object on the deck, he paused.

"Have you lost something? May I help?" he inquired.

Alicia turned her big brown eyes on him gratefully.

"I've lost an earring," she said with a disarming smile.

A short and unsuccessful search for the fictitious earring led unerringly to a date for that evening in the third mate's cabin.

"Easy, wasn't it?" I commented when Alicia later reported the success of her mission.

The captain had already shown me over the ship – with a pause for more intimate conversation in his own cabin – and we had established a promising relationship that would see us through the final leg of the voyage to Oslo.

Later that night, when Alicia returned to our cabin, she said: "When I was with the mate, Carl, there was a knock at the door. It was the boss – I could only see his legs because I was hiding under a rug below the bunk, but I recognised his voice.

"He was telling the mate with an intimidating gesture to make sure he and the rest of the crew keep clear of the passengers. 'Saving them, no doubt, for himself,' said Carl when he had gone."

I sniggered. "While I was with Knut – that's his name, by the way – he kept saying he hoped my poor friend didn't mind being on her own all this time. If only he knew!"

Alicia said: "Apparently he's a real tartar. The crew hate him, according to Carl."

"I'm not surprised," I replied. "He's a masterful man as I found to my cost . . . By the way, did you know Knut is the Norwegian version of Canute? Very fitting for a tyrant bent on mastery of the waves!"

"Hmm. I can imagine he has his way not only with the waves but also with his women. If we get bored before the trip ends we'll swap."

"Agreed," I said.

We did not get bored. Some evenings Alicia and I played three-handed bridge in the lounge with the captain. These occasions were very fraught as Alicia had never played before and the captain was angry when she could not remember which cards had gone.

"You must keep count, you silly girl," he shouted. "You are pretty useless at this game."

It was a humbling experience for her, and I realised that for the first time in her life she felt small and inadequate. I felt sorry not only for her but also for myself. The captain's bad temper ruined the fun for all of us, so we often tried to sidetrack him into telling rude stories or naughty jokes. When his temper was really frayed, Alicia would suddenly remember something important she had to do in our cabin and leave the lounge.

"I know a more exciting sort of bridge than this rotten card game," she said crossly as she got up from the table one evening.

The captain didn't twig what she was up to, though to me it was blatantly obvious that she was on her way to join the third mate on watch. She told me later: "He's got a much better hand to play, with plenty of tricks."

When the captain and the mate were on duty we had the endlessly fascinating sea to watch, parts of the boat to explore and our four fellow passengers – middle-aged Scandinavian couples – to chat with in our halting Norwegian. We had learnt the language at London evening classes before resigning from our secretarial jobs to set forth in search of employment and fun in the Frozen North, but it did not yet trip easily off our tongues.

The other passengers didn't quite approve of us because they suspected dimly that we were up to no good during our long absences from the lounge, where they sat mulling over politics and world affairs. The latest topic was the recent death of Stalin, on the same day as his fellow countryman, the composer Prokofiev. The most heated arguments were about the conduct of the war, a subject which cropped up at every mealtime.

Everyone made an effort to be polite to us and include us in the conversation whenever possible.

"So this is your first visit to our country?" said pompous old Herr Jensen during dinner one evening as we all sat at the captain's table eating fiskeboller – a disgusting dish of fishballs which the Norwegians were gobbling up with relish. Disguised as hard-boiled eggs, they lay innocently on our plates and we had eaten several before we realised what they were.

"Yes," I replied, fiddling with a fishball and wishing I were not so hungry.

"How do you plan to spend your time and what sort of jobs will you take?" Herr Jensen inquired.

"Aha," I replied enigmatically. "We shall have to see what turns up." I winked at Alicia.

The captain was peeling an orange with what seemed to me excessive concentration. I was annoyed because he was ignoring me, so I turned my attention to the chief engineer, an obsequious gentleman with false teeth which he kept snapping excitedly at Alicia and me in turn.

Alicia was telling Fru Jensen about our unsuccessful efforts, launched from England, to secure jobs in Norway.

"We advertised in *Aftenposten* and the only reply we got was from an 85-year-old bachelor who wanted us to be his housekeepers. But he said he could only afford to pay 50 kroner (then £2.50) a week for the two of us, and what can you do with that?"

"Quite so," agreed Fru Jensen, helping herself to another slice of brown *geitost*, the delicious goat's milk cheese which we thought tasted rather like fudge.

The captain was still peeling his orange with great care. I was furious and leaned towards the chief engineer. He quivered and his teeth clicked like castanets. I felt I had gone too far and leant back before they could drop on my lap.

"Yes," Alicia was saying blandly. "We want to find some really interesting work when we get to Oslo. Something not too boring that will enable us to get around a bit and see the country. I don't want anything too menial, though, as I'm very well connected."

"Snob!" I said softly, for her ears only.

The stewardess came to clear away the plates. The captain put his hand down firmly on his pile of orange peel and told her to leave it on the table. I had no idea he was so fond of oranges, though I had noticed a large crateful on the bridge – part of the cargo which had been taken on at Bilbao.

The other passengers were leaving the table, lurching a little as a result of the wine and wild waves. The chief engineer was lingering hopefully, and when Alicia left in quest of some pastime he followed her out.

The captain and I were alone. For the first time since the meal started he looked at me and said: "How's this for a mini-sculpture?"

He held up the orange peel, which he had turned inside out and fashioned skilfully with his fruit knife. He roared with laughter at my expression. I was disgusted but made a mental note to reproduce the mannikin –

whose focal point was a length of the central pith – for my aunt at Christmas.

When I reached the door of our cabin I noticed a pungent smell. Surely Alicia didn't smoke cheroots? I opened the door softly. Just as I thought . . .

"You might have told me you were entertaining after dinner," I grumbled when I returned to our cabin later. "I nearly had to spend a freezing two hours under the lifeboats."

"But someone came to your rescue?" Alicia said mischievously.

"Well, the captain's cabin is the best on the ship. The only trouble is that people keep blowing whistles down the speaking tube. It's most distracting."

The captain's whistle was not the only sudden noise which caught me off balance. Nosing about on the bridge while the master attended to his duties, I was intrigued to spot in large letters: "Full fart." I was opening my mouth to ask the meaning of this bizarre command when the ship's hooter emitted such a loud blast that I nearly had a heart attack.

"That's certainly the fullest fart I've ever heard," I exclaimed. "But are you permitted this luxury only on the bridge?"

The captain fell about laughing. "It's true we have got a tail wind today, my sweet," he said. "But that sign has nothing to do with the ship's hooter or anyone's bodily function. It merely means 'full steam ahead'."

Much invigorated by this absurd experience, I decided to have a bath.

The ship was rolling violently in a Force 9 gale as I staggered to the small bathroom and climbed with difficulty into the tub. The water kept sloshing from one end to the other, and I was busily trying to de-soap myself when I became aware of an eye at the keyhole and a faint snapping sound.

I reached for my toothbrush and, with a swift movement, jabbed it through the hole.

"Ouch!" yelled a voice. The Norwegian expletive "Pokker ta det!" followed.

"And fishballs to you," I shouted as I retrieved my toothbrush, grabbed a lump of soap and rammed it into the keyhole.

Lunchtime came and the ship was still behaving like a bucking bronco. The stewardess was placing little waxed cardboard pots at various vantage points on the floor. I asked her what they were for.

"Fiskesuppe," was her chilling reply.

I recoiled. What on earth did she mean? Was fish soup really on the lunch menu? And were we to eat it on the floor because the storm was expected to get worse? Either way it was an ill omen.

The stewardess saw my long face and laughed.

"Yuk!" she mouthed. Her theatrical and eloquent mime left no room for doubt: these were sick bowls and the storm was going to worsen.

She started pouring water over the tablecloth so that the dishes would not slip about. Wooden frames would come later if things really hotted up. Fortunately none of us needed to take advantage of the cardboard pots, but the very sight of them had put me off my food. The last straw was when the odour of fish soup wafted into my over-sensitive nostrils. The pots were a doubly evil portent after all, then.

To take my mind off my sorrows I remarked nonchalantly during a lull in the conversation: "I learned a new word today, 'pokker'. Can anyone tell me what it means?"

Next to me there was a choking sound from the chief engineer and I noticed for the first time that one of his eyes was red and puffy.

"Aha – so it was you," I said grimly, turning sharply

towards him and upsetting my steaming bowl of fish soup over his trousers.

He leapt up with his favourite oath, stamped his foot and made hastily for the door, muttering something about the engines.

"Tut, tut!" said Fru Jensen disapprovingly. "What a naughty tantrum from such a nice man."

Alicia asked me later, when we were sitting on deck admiring the magnificent landscape as we entered the Oslofjord, what this titillating little lunchtime drama was all about.

"I just discovered a naughty word this morning, that's all, when that horrid chief engineer was spying on me in my bath."

Suddenly there was an enormous bang and the ship shuddered to a halt. Men were running about all over the decks, shouting, and the captain was galloping like a huge bull towards the engine room. He disappeared through a tiny hatch in a cloud of smoke.

"What has happened?" I called to the bos'n as he sped past.

"Explosion in the engine room," he yelled.

It took an hour and a half to get the ship moving again.

"And all because that fool of a chief turned the wrong valve," the captain explained later. "Said it was because of his sore eye. How he got it I don't know – someone must have taken a poke at him."

"Looks more like a toothbrush," I said caustically as I walked off, leaving the captain looking mystified.

As we approached Oslo along the thickly wooded slopes of the fjord, Alicia and I saw little of the third mate and the captain until it was time to go ashore. Then, as we were preparing to go down the gangplank, I had a message to go to Knut's cabin.

"Surely not now?" I said to Alicia.

When I reached the cabin the captain was in a jocular mood. In his hand he held a gaily wrapped box, about a foot long.

"For you, min kjæreste, to remind you of our happy times," he grinned, nibbling my ear. "And here's another small memento of your trip," he added, pressing what seemed to be a wad of notes into my hand. A quick hug and he was gone.

I didn't open my present until Alicia and I were ashore in a quiet cafe. We ordered mugs of hot chocolate and I drained mine before tearing eagerly at the wrappings. Was it a handbag, I wondered, with perhaps some money to go with it?

As I lifted off the lid of the box Alicia started to giggle. "What's that?" she asked.

I stared, nonplussed. A huge marzipan pig was lying in a nest of crinkly cellophane. Oh, well, I still had his other gift, the wad of paper that felt like 100 kroner notes.

I ripped it open, eager for the sight of the loot. The wad of paper unravelled like a concertina. It was a folding picture strip of Port Said, pre-war by the look of it.

"You've been done good and proper," said Alicia in a mocking voice.

I tried to hide my chagrin by changing the subject.

"What's the time? Will the labour exchange be open yet?"

Alicia flashed under my nose a huge gold watch which was strapped to her tiny wrist.

"There," she said smugly. "See for yourself."

Amid the 18-carat gold I had a dazzling impression of the astronomical clock at Hampton Court Palace, and I noticed it was March 10th and full moon.

"Where did you get that?" I gasped.

"I won it last night."

"The third mate?"

She nodded.

"And I thought I had won the toss," I said glumly.

We walked out of the cafe, leaving the marzipan pig on the table standing guard over our empty mugs.

The picture strip of Port Said fluttered to the floor.

2
Fishballs!

The labour exchange was presided over by a sullen woman in a shiny black satin overall. All the other women wore shiny black overalls, too.

"Well, what can you do?" she demanded as she prepared to take down our particulars.

"Nothing special," I replied cheerfully. "We could do housework or look after children, I suppose."

The woman gave a meaningful glance at our white hands and said: "Humph." Then she asked for our papers.

"Papers?" we echoed.

"Papers – references," she said tartly. "From previous employers."

"Ah – no, not as Norwegian housemaids. But we have English office references, if they would do," Alicia said.

"Hardly the same line of work and I don't think your Norwegian is up to office work in Oslo," she commented dryly. "Still, I'll try a few people."

She tried, by telephone. "I have two English girls who want to be house helps. No, they haven't any references and their Norwegian isn't very good, but . . . No? Thank you."

For three days we called to see her, each time with no success.

We also toured the hotels and restaurants in the hope of getting jobs as scullery hands or chambermaids, but were told to come back after Easter when everyone had returned to Oslo after the universal holiday exodus to the hills and mountains.

The British Embassy proved an abortive source of employment, but we fared much better at the American Embassy and each ended up with the offer of a job looking after horribly spoilt little boys – and the threat of being taken back to America and assimilated into the families for good.

Alicia was tempted, but I said firmly: "We didn't come to Norway to be swallowed up by Americans."

The overalled woman at the labour exchange finally sent us to another department to see if we could get outdoor work instead.

"That might be better," said Alicia. "I'd certainly rather work for a virile outdoor type than a bossy housewife who wants to treat us as skivvies."

The only job the agricultural section could suggest was as gardeners in a dreary industrial town some way from Oslo. When we went there for interviews the "virile outdoor types" turned out to be weedy old men with grabbing hands.

"But it may be this or nothing," I said morosely. "Perhaps we should have a go."

Alicia plucked up courage and went off for a quick trial with one of the less objectionable looking men. Quick it certainly was, for she reappeared 10 minutes later looking flushed and rumpled.

"It wasn't the weeds in his flowerbeds I had to deal with – it was him," she said indignantly. "Talk about bindweed – he was all over me."

Meanwhile I had been enticed into another garden and ordered to scale a tall plum tree with a wicked-looking saw to test my pruning skills. I looked at the tree, at the saw, at my would-be employer standing arms akimbo with a nasty grin on his face; and I chickened out.

We decided gardening wasn't our metier after all. This rough outdoor work was obviously best left to the Danish girls who flocked to Norway to tend animals and labour on the land.

By this time our confidence was in tatters. Feeling thoroughly deflated, we went back to the domestic section of the labour exchange, where the stern woman almost managed a smile.

"I've found a nice little temporary job for one of you," she said. "It's only for a week, but it will be better than nothing."

She told us a party of English school pupils were visiting Oslo on a cultural exchange with some Norwegian children, and one of the local weekly newspapers, hearing two English girls were seeking jobs, was keen for one of us to cover the event as a temporary assignment.

"So which of you will it be, then?" she asked.

Before Alicia could open her mouth I had put up my hand like a schoolgirl wanting to be first to answer Teacher's question. I had always fancied myself as a reporter and now was my chance to prove myself.

"It's you, then," said the woman. "You start right away."

She told me to present myself to the editor of the newspaper in a seedy suburb of Oslo. Alicia could barely bring herself to speak to me, so annoyed was she at my coup in securing this plum, if temporary, job. She would have been less envious had she foreseen that I was about to be jettisoned into an even more far-fetched occupation than the mere brandishing of a saw.

As I stepped on to the articulated tram which was to bear me off to my new mini-career, Alicia grudgingly wished me luck.

"Just think of how you'll be enjoying yourself while I'm hard at work," I said consolingly. "You'll have all the men to yourself."

It took me half an hour to find the grubby little office above a grubby little shop which served as the editorial headquarters of the newspaper. A timid, elfin-faced girl called Hilde showed me into the editor's room. This poky, musty-smelling hovel was so crammed from floor to ceiling with unsold back copies of newspapers, tattered reference books, discarded typewriters and boxes of stationery that I didn't at first notice the man standing beside one of the bookcases.

The editor was white-haired and irascible, with a malevolent expression. I wondered why he was wearing earphones and pointing a little black box at me as he shouted: "Right, girl, you'll do. Have you got a notebook? Come on, girl, speak up – I'm rather deaf."

The box he was holding under my nose was wired up to his earphones, and I realised it was an amplifier. I yelled into it: "Yes, Sir, I have a notebook and pencil."

The valves in his black box oscillated with an ear-splitting screech and he leapt back with a few pithy oaths, clutching his headphones.

"For God's sake, no need to shout, girl! Do you want to wreck my hearing altogether?" he howled. "And none of that 'Sir' nonsense here. Just you get on with your job and all will be well."

I cowered and his manner softened.

"Never mind me, girl, my bark is worse than my bite. Now let's get down to business. Our reporter Eyolf will show you the ropes and then you are on your own. You'll find the bicycle in the shed at the back of the shop."

My heart skipped a beat. "Bicycle?" I stammered. "What do you mean?"

"Your bicycle, girl – how do you think you're going to get around without it?"

"Oh . . . I see . . . yes, well . . ." I said querulously.

The door burst open and in slunk a one-armed man

wearing a shabby coat and a black patch over one eye. So this was what newspaper people were like, I thought – black boxes, black eye patches, black hearts, too, no doubt.

"This is Eyolf, our reporter," said the editor. "He'll show you what's what. And no hanky-panky, Eyolf, she's too genteel, and anyhow she'll be too busy."

I looked with respect at this one-armed, one-eyed Lothario. His sexual prowess was not diminished by his physical disabilities, then. And what did the deaf old editor mean, 'genteel'?

Eyolf looked at his editor, then at me, and said: "She may be genteel, Oswald, but she's a tasty titbit. We'll see about the hanky-panky."

Oswald swiped at his reporter with a folded newspaper and told us both to get out.

The next hour was spent in Eyolf's little cubbyhole, where he explained the fundamentals of journalism which, in the normal course of events, I would have picked up over several years.

"You go off now, you pretty little thing, and bring your write-up of the day's happenings to me at home," he said. "I can then go over it with you and see where you've gone wrong."

I asked him why I had been chosen to cover the children's visit when it was a job a Norwegian reporter could easily have done.

"Because I refused to do it," he said. "I hate kids. It would have been bad enough traipsing round after Norwegian children, but having to interview English brats would be hell. So Oswald has agreed to let me translate your story instead."

I thought this a long-winded procedure but at least it had got me the job, so who was I to complain about Eyolf's stubbornness?

I went downstairs and found the cycle – a rusty old

machine with a saddle as sharp as the editor's tongue. It was all I could do to mount as the saddle was too high and the nut too rusty to lower it.

At last I wobbled off down the busy street on the wrong side of the road, narrowly missing colliding with a tram. The driver leant out and gave me a brusque ticking-off while the passengers sat and tut-tutted.

The traffic terrified me, but eventually I reached my destination, a church hall where the British school-children were attending a lecture in English on Norse legends. They were a noisy, boisterous crowd, not in the least interested in the antics of the Vikings, their Valhalla, their poison sea and their kinky gods. However, I interviewed them as best I could about where they came from and what they thought about Norway, and then took a few photographs with the bulky old camera the editor had lent me, which looked as though it belonged in a museum.

I decided there was no useful purpose in staying any longer so I set off for Eyolf's apartment on the outskirts of the city. By now it was early evening and I was peckish. Eyolf welcomed me into his flat and offered me rolls and *geitost* to ward off the hunger pangs until I could get a proper meal.

"I've never done this sort of work before," I said nervously as I got out the large notebook in which I had jotted down the salient facts of my story.

"You're doing fine," he said. "You're good at taking things down, aren't you?"

"Not that good," I said, suspecting a *double entendre*. He was not deterred but moved closer and put his face next to mine as we peered into the pages of my notebook and tried to decipher my scribble.

Two hours passed before we managed, between us, to draft out some sort of coherent report for his newspaper – "and I've still got to translate it," he said.

I got up to go. "I really must get back or my girlfriend will be wondering what's happened to me."

"Surely she can get by on her own? We have a lot to talk about, and you'll need a bit more instruction in your new job."

"But it's only going to last for a week," I said. "It's not as if I'm taking up journalism as a career."

"Never mind that – with a bit of encouragement you may find you like it. Then you can try to get a job on an English newspaper when you go home."

After my experiences on the bicycle and in the church hall, I didn't think this was likely. But Eyolf's one arm was round me, his one blue eye was twinkling, and I weakened.

"All right, then, I'll stay a bit longer and learn a bit more."

Three hours later I arrived back at the youth hostel where Alicia and I were staying.

"You've been a long time. I thought you'd vanished into limbo," she said huffily. "Did you enjoy your reporting?"

"Yes, in a way," I replied.

When I recounted my day's adventures she was agog.

"About this one-eyed Eyolf: one arm, one eye. How is he so perky when he has only one of everything?"

"One is enough, I can assure you. And he can get up to more mischief with his one arm than most men with two. It certainly wasn't a handicap. He lost his arm and eye in the war while taking part in a raid to sabotage a Nazi ammunition dump, by the way. He's made up for his loss by being extra macho ever since."

I was pleased to hear that Alicia had not been idle while I was occupied on my journalistic enterprise. She had been dallying down at the docks watching the big ships and flirting with the big sailors. One had taken her out for a meal and made a date for the following day –

"and as the ship is in dock for a week that should tide me over until your little caper has ended".

Next day saw me bright and early at the office. The editor praised me for my write-up and told me I was to spend today at a local school, where the visiting children were attending a symposium, again in English, on the history of the Norwegian monarchy.

I was chuffed with his praise – I didn't confess that Eyolf had masterminded my article – but viewed the day's programme with misgiving.

"Do I have to sit through the whole lecture?" I asked.

Oswald had turned away and did not hear me. I repeated my question into his little black box.

"Yes," he said firmly. "It's all good practice and you'll find it interesting, anyway. Besides, it will keep you out of Eyolf's clutches. You beware of him, girl – he's a fast worker, arm or no arm. He'll make mincemeat of a gullible little thing like you."

"Oh, thank you for warning me," I simpered. "I'll be specially careful, I promise you."

"Good girl. Now off you go. You know the way – it's over that steep hill to the fjord, then turn left."

With my big notebook tucked into my pocket, I set off on the clattering old bike. The traffic was just as hairy as yesterday until I reached the edge of the city. Then came a long, steep hill and I had to push my bike as it had no gears to ease the hard slog.

Breathing a sigh of relief when I reached the brow of the hill, I perched myself gingerly on the frightful saddle and pedalled furiously to get up enough speed to take me to the bottom and round the corner to the school. Faster and faster I went, the wind in my hair, jubilation in my heart. I was a newspaper reporter, and it was downhill all the way to my next job.

A cat ran into the road ahead and I braked hard.

Nothing happened. I squeezed the brakes even harder. Still no response. Swerving violently to avoid the cat, I skidded off the road, across a short stretch of rough ground and into the fjord.

An elderly woman hurried over to help extricate me from the waterweeds and the twisted wreck of the bicycle.

"Dear me," she said in consternation. "What a mess your clothes are in! And just look at what you've done to your cycle! And what's that floating away in the water?"

I turned to look. My big reporter's notebook – my pride and joy, my status symbol – was well on its way out to sea, its one-day jottings blurring as the rippling wavelets washed over its almost virgin pages.

A kindly builder with a tip-up lorry volunteered to transport me and my bicycle back to the office. There he unloaded the heap of bent metal and leant it against the shop wall. I stomped upstairs, dripping seaweedy water all over the carpet.

The editor was not pleased to see me. He was even less pleased when I took him downstairs and showed him what remained of the cycle.

"That's going to cost a pretty penny to repair," he raved. "I'll have to deduct it from your week's wages, so there won't be much left for you, girl. And why aren't you at the lecture? You could have got there on foot – it's just round the corner from where you crashed."

I glared at him. "You know what you can do with your job, don't you? As for my wages, you can get yourself a hot sausage with them – that's just about all they will buy."

He was about to find out just how genteel I was. I stormed out of the room, slamming the plate glass door behind me. As I turned into the street I was rewarded by the sound of shattering glass.

I decided reporting wasn't my metier.

Things could only get better, Alicia and I agreed – and sure enough, the next day the woman at the labour exchange greeted us with an animated smile. I had been worrying that she might have had a complaint from the newspaper editor about the cycle and the glass door, but my fears were obviously unfounded. He must have had a guilty conscience for palming me off with such a dud machine – unless, of course, he was just too busy catching up on the missed symposium.

"I've found something that really will suit you, and it's for the two of you," the labour exchange woman was saying. "There's a large house half an hour from Oslo where two housemaids are needed. Fru Olsen has agreed to take you both although you have no papers."

Our pay was to be 37 kroner (then £1.85) a week all found, which did not compare favourably with the 60 kroner a week we had been offered by the Americans. But we were sure we could manage on it and our confidence was not misplaced, for we had a 13 kroner increase by the time our first pay day arrived.

Neither of us was good at arithmetic so we were thankful the exchange rate of 20 kroner to the pound – with one krone the equivalent of one shilling (5p) – made calculations easy for us.

We packed our bags that afternoon and set off by bus for a tiny hamlet a few miles up the Oslo fjord.

"Into service with a smile," said Alicia breezily as she consulted her astronomical watch. "We'll probably get there just in time to wash up after lunch."

The house was indeed imposing, built in the old Norwegian log cabin style and set in a clearing among pine forests. It was surrounded by scaffolding, over which hordes of handsome workmen swarmed.

I nudged Alicia. "Do you see what I see?"

She was already scanning the scaffolding with an

expert eye. "Bags me that one," she said, indicating a plumpish man wielding a plumber's wrench.

"Okay, the painter will suit me," I replied. The painter was tall and florid with a sad expression.

While we were giving our prospective victims the once-over, the back door opened and an ascetic-looking man emerged, wearing an enormous smile and plus fours which looked several sizes too big.

He was carrying what we thought was a large butterfly net. We later learned that it was to catch flying beetles so small that only he could see them as they flitted about, their tiny wings iridescent in the sunlight.

"Good afternoon, welcome to our home. I am Herr Olsen," he beamed as he shook us warmly by the hand.

Alicia gave me a significant look. As we were following him into the house she whispered: "We must keep clear of married men, and anyway he's not suitable."

I agreed. Herr Olsen was thoroughly wholesome, and we were to discover that he was one of those rare Norwegian males who did not have seduction in mind every time he saw a woman.

Fru Olsen was a tall, willowy woman with a vague manner and mournful face. She seemed nervous of her husband, who ordered her about as though she were a pet dog.

"Show them to their rooms, Anna," he commanded. "Then come down to the study and help me label my beetles."

If the house was superb, so were the workmen imported from the far valleys to modernise it. They were living in two of the bedrooms in the main wing, which was practically being rebuilt.

"This is your room," Fru Olsen told me as she drifted across the landing. "Our room is on one side and the workmen are on the other side, so you won't be all on your own."

No, I thought – I can guarantee that. Ten pairs of blue eyes were boring into me through an open door as I passed by with Fru Olsen.

I could see that Alicia was miffed to find that her room was in the servants' wing, where the renovation had already been completed, but she made a pathetic attempt at nonchalance as she showed me the radio beside her bed. She had noticed I had no such luxury.

"I won't be needing a radio," I said spitefully. "I've got other entertainment in mind. I shall have plenty of wavelengths to choose from."

"All but one. Remember the plumber's mine."

We unpacked our few belongings and donned the white aprons we found in our cupboards, feeling much relieved that we were not having to wear the ghastly black satin overalls we had seen in the labour exchange. Then, ignoring the small white triangles which we assumed were some sort of headgear – "but I can't imagine how you fix them," said Alicia – we went downstairs.

In the spacious Swedish-designed kitchen, which boasted every modern labour-saving device, we met Ingrid, the children's nanny, who, like us, was in her early 20s. With one hand she was shovelling fish pudding – an unappetising variation of fishballs which looked like white blancmange – down the throat of a bawling female toddler, while with the other she was chastising a small boy. An older girl was raiding the biscuit drawer.

Alicia eyed the brats with distrust.

"What cute little children," she said with a hypocritical smirk.

"Yes, aren't they?" said Ingrid, giving the boy another slap. "This is Sigurd, he's five. Elsa over there is nine and little Hedvig is nearly two. You'll be looking after them on my days off."

"How nice," Alicia said without conviction. "I'm sure we'll all be great friends."

It was obvious the children did not share her confidence in our future good relationship. The two older ones scowled at us and Elsa skipped round the room chanting something that sounded like "shookyhewer". We guessed her words were unflattering, if not downright rude, because Ingrid gave her a hearty smack.

Elsa, unrepentant, asked why those funny women had such a silly accent.

"Because they come from England, dear," explained Ingrid. "So you'll have to speak slowly and clearly for them."

Elsa sniffed, stuffed another biscuit into her mouth and ran into the garden, followed by her brother. Hedvig, the baby, had taken a fancy to me and was pulling my hair as hard as she could, playfully but painfully.

When the two older children had gone out I asked Ingrid what "shookyhewer" meant, just in case I encountered the phrase later. At first she was reluctant to divulge the meaning, but when pressed she told us the child had dubbed us "tjukk i hue", meaning "thick in the head" – in other words, stupid.

Right, I thought – I'll repay that little scallywag by fair means or foul, probably by putting her to bed an hour early on Ingrid's day off. I turned my attention to more important matters – food. It struck me as unusual that the family had, judging by the debris on the table, been eating a cooked meal at four o'clock. Was it late lunch or early supper?

Ingrid explained that they were having an early lunch today because Fru Olsen was going out in the evening.

"Early? Early lunch, did you say?" I said.

Ingrid looked puzzled. "Yes, of course – *middag*. We usually eat around five o'clock."

"But I thought '*middag*' meant 'midday'," I insisted.

"It does. But in Norway we have *middag* in the late afternoon or early evening."

Alicia and I decided that *middag* was the most outrageous misnomer we had ever encountered as the meal was usually eaten between about 3pm and 6pm – but never as early as midday.

"They're obviously quite scatty, the Norwegians," I said, without malice. "They not only eat *middag* at teatime or later, they also say 'Morgen' all day long for 'Good morning', even in the evening."

We agreed, though, that the Norwegians were irresistibly charming – and, more important, extremely handsome.

"Which is all that matters to us," said Alicia.

"Your trouble is that you have a one-track mind," I scoffed at her. "You're not just a simple country girl like me."

"And you have – or had – a marzipan pig to prove it," she countered. "Even your mother couldn't object to a pig as a token of, shall we say, respect."

"At least a marzipan pig isn't dutiable. I hope you'll manage to get that ridiculous clock of yours past the Customs when we go home."

I was beginning to wish I hadn't discarded the wretched pig. Norway, with its cold, exhilarating air, was giving me a ravenous appetite, and we had missed *middag*. I consoled myself with the thought that we had also missed that ghastly fish pudding.

As Alicia and I busied ourselves with the few light tasks Fru Olsen had allotted us – "you don't look as though you are used to working, so don't tire yourselves" – we wondered when the next meal would be. By seven o'clock I was getting anxious.

We helped Ingrid put the children to bed and learned that Sigurd hated water, the baby loved it to the point of obsession, and getting Elsa to bed was a feat of superhuman skill requiring determination, physical agility and some degree of cunning in seeking out her hiding places.

At eight o'clock Fru Olsen said, as she was leaving the house with her husband, that we could knock off. She explained that our duties would normally end much earlier, after we had cleared up after *middag*. Still no mention of supper.

"Don't we have to get the supper?" I inquired.

"Supper?"

"Yes, the evening meal."

"Oh, we don't have an evening meal."

I paled. "You mean you don't eat anything after *middag*?"

"No, of course not. But if you are hungry you can get yourselves something to eat if you like," she added absent-mindedly.

We needed no second bidding. We found eggs and made an omelette, and followed it with a large plateful of berries – an indeterminate species picked by Fru Olsen in the woods near by. We hoped they were not poisonous.

"She's so vague," said Alicia. "You never know."

We survived the berries and the night passed without incident. All was quiet in the workmen's room next to mine and I later discovered the reason. They had gone off for the weekend to their homes in the valleys.

Next morning Alicia and I were starving. We cooked the breakfast, a simple meal of eggs and coffee, and sustained ourselves mid-morning with wheatmeal biscuits and brown goat's cheese. We asked Fru Olsen what we should prepare for lunch, hoping we could make an early start on it.

"Today," she announced, "we are going to have fishballs."

We both flinched. "F-f-f-fishballs?" I stuttered. "I thought you had those yesterday."

"No, that was fish pudding," she said grandly. "We never have the same thing two days running."

Middag in the Olsen household, we were to learn, never was the same two days running. One day it would be fish pudding, the next day fishballs and the third day hot boiled sausages. These three dishes were occasionally varied with meatballs or a type of stew which we found equally distasteful.

The first course was never followed by a dessert because Herr Olsen had a tiny appetite. As he and his wife ate with us in the kitchen – the dining room was still under renovation – we had to suffer in silence until he had left the table. We then pounced on a pot of cream in the fridge and found some fruit to eat with it.

"I suppose the cream is for their coffee, but I'm sure they can spare a little," said Alicia.

One day we were all having *middag* in the kitchen when guests arrived unexpectedly. We servants had to leave the table halfway through our meal, so we piled our dishes with food and carried them into the dining-room to finish eating, standing up and balancing our plates on some old boxes lying around in the half-empty room.

"Where else but Norway could it happen that the servants eat in the dining-room and the guests in the kitchen?" I said.

Next day Fru Olsen suggested we should have pancakes for lunch as her husband was particularly partial to them. We were delighted to think there would be a second course for a change.

"And what will we be having for the first course?" I asked.

"Pancakes *are* the first course," said Fru Olsen.

So on pancake days we had a couple of pancakes
each, eaten with jam, and that was that. We supplemented this frugal repast by raids on the larder, which
had been sanctioned by Fru Olsen, luckily, and pre-
vented us fading away like naughty Kaspar in the
Struwwelpeter cautionary tale.

3
Cosy Evenings

We settled happily into our role as Norwegian housemaids, and on the whole our duties were light. We rose at 7am and our day's work normally ended after *middag*, which was why we made sure the meal was served as early as possible.

Alicia did what little cooking was needed, even baking a birthday cake for Elsa from a Norwegian recipe the day after we arrived, while I, a peasant at heart, preferred to do the cleaning.

We shared one of the more tiresome tasks – washing the vast areas of wooden floor with liberal sloppings of cold water mixed with ammonia, which then had to be mopped dry. This was supposed to prevent the light-coloured wood from darkening.

Only one thing seriously marred our serenity – the telephone. We dreaded hearing it ring because one of us had to answer it if no one else was within earshot. The ensuing exchange of words was always a disaster. Try as we might we could never persuade the caller to say: "Please may I speak to so-and-so." We assumed it would be for Herr Olsen, but such a suggestion on our part was always met with a torrent of words, never a name, and pleas that the caller should speak more slowly were always ignored.

Alicia and I developed a strategy for telephone evasion. Whichever of us first heard the tinkling of the bell would furtively vanish into the basement on the pretext of doing some laundry, so the fleetest of foot was the victor in this battle of the telephone. In the basement lurked another menace – a powerful American automatic washing machine. It leapt into life with a whooshing scream which never failed to catch us unawares and frighten us half to death. We christened it the Devil Machine.

A more benevolent domestic utility was also housed in the basement – a walk-in deep freeze the size of a small room. We knew its store of goodies included huge packs of frozen raspberries – many picked by us in the forest – and Fru Olsen dished out large helpings on special occasions.

We did our best to make sure these occasions became more frequent. Fortunately, Fru Olsen was a quick learner and it wasn't long before she took to joining us for *aftens*, the evening snack which we inaugurated to ward off night starvation.

The menu usually consisted of boiled eggs, ham, toast and butter, brown biscuits and *geitost*, redcurrants and whipped cream, and sometimes cornflakes, followed by coffee. Herr Olsen also enjoyed these mini feasts, and when he was in a genial mood they would be taken into the *peisestue*, his study. This was decorated in traditional style with gaily painted woodwork and we would eat in front of the log fire blazing on the *peis*, the large open corner hearth.

During these "cosy evenings", as he called them, we were treated to a viewing of his beetles, which were displayed in glass-topped cases like microscopic butterflies. We were also regaled with a selection of his "Scottish stories", which always began: "It was a Scottish man and he should . . ."

His favourite was about the Scottish man "who should go to Italy on honeymoon" but who left his bride at home because she had been there before.

These extra snacks and the titbits Alicia and I helped

ourselves to during the day to tide us over until *middag* resulted in huge grocery bills, but Fru Olsen never complained. Alicia and I, too, paid a price for our gluttony – we began to lose our svelte figures.

"You're getting fat," said Alicia, eyeing me critically.

"You, too," I retaliated, stung by the insult.

We both hoped it was our imagination until a friend visiting us from England said nastily: "You're fatter." And to twist the knife in the wound, she added: "I'm going to ring up your boyfriends and tell them."

Alicia and I were overcome at the sight of so much butter, cheese and cream in the Olsen fridge. Back home rationing was not due to end until the following year, though tea and sweets had recently come off ration. Cheese had been cut to 1oz a week and the meat ration increased to permit people to spend 1s 7d (8p) a week on their allowance.

Here, Fru Olsen bought pork chops which were each the size of a week's ration in England but they were reserved mainly for visitors. The butter was used for frying, which we thought extravagant as it cost eight kroner (40p) a kilo, four times the price of the very palatable margarine.

Alicia and I earned Fru Olsen's eternal gratitude for educating her in the delights of roast beef and Yorkshire pudding. She had never even heard of roast potatoes, and on the occasions when she and her husband entertained friends to a meal we had to cook this traditional English fare, which was enthused over by everyone. Indeed, we suspected that Fru Olsen was so proud of the tasty new offering that people were invited to the house more frequently just so they could partake of the wonderful roast beef and Yorkshire pud.

If Fru Olsen was generous in the provision of nourishment, her husband was even more so in making sure we had all the small comforts of life. One day he brought us each a set of four English national newspapers of that day's date – a feat which bordered on the miraculous as they were normally several days old.

He subsequently ordered a regular copy of the *Daily Telegraph* for us each, but was unable to repeat the same-day success.

Not to be outdone, Fru Olsen gave us each a Norwegian grammar, dictionary and picture book with lovely photographs of the Norwegian countryside. The dictionary was a boon except that no genders were given for the nouns – an unpardonable omission on the part of the publishers, and one we subsequently found repeated even in larger dictionaries.

"How daft, having no gender," I snorted.

"I know. I met someone like that once, in Brighton – very disappointing," said Alicia dreamily.

Fru Olsen also bought an oil painting of a Sussex scene for each of our bedrooms. She was an ardent admirer of the English countryside and its magnificent deciduous trees and ordered a dozen landscapes from Britain to adorn the walls of the house.

She also gave Alicia and me a large bottle of expensive hand lotion "because it is my fault you are ruining your hands".

Fru Olsen was very sensitive about things that were "nasty", which she pronounced "naysty". She had no hesitation in dismissing our early efforts at decorating *smørbrød* as "naysty" and was eager to initiate us into the mysteries of perfecting these delectable open sandwiches. When she was having a party, we would spend hours constructing these little works of art under her supervision and had to make sure the colour schemes accorded with her artistic requirements. If, for instance, we put brown *geitost* with the wrong savoury titbit, she would say: "Oh no, you can't have those colours together, they are very naysty."

Certain members of her family, too, were frequently "naysty". Every few days Fru Olsen would entice one of us from our chores for a heart-to-heart in the deserted dining-room about whoever was causing her anxiety at that moment.

Mostly it was her husband, who was quite often "very naysty". The two of them never argued, partly because she was so docile, and he never looked elsewhere for female companionship, but for some reason we could not fathom she lived in constant dread that he would divorce her. Rightly or wrongly we had the impression that it was merely a question of "I turn round three times and divorce thee". We had to talk to her like agony aunts and assure her that we were convinced she had nothing to fear. After this, her habitual mournful manner would brighten, if only for a few days.

Sometimes it was her elder daughter who was "naysty". Elsa was a wilful but likeable child, and our only complaint about her was the difficulty of catching her at bedtime on Ingrid's day off. When we finally had her safely under her duvet she would nag us to read to her from *Winnie the Pooh*. As it was in Norwegian, we were never sure whether she really enjoyed hearing the tale or whether she just wanted to have a laugh at our atrocious accents as we had not yet mastered the subtleties of pronunciation.

It was even harder to catch Sigurd, whose trump card at bedtime was vanishing into the farm cottage opposite where all the workmen used to congregate in the evening. One of us had to run the gauntlet of their good-natured banter as we played an undignified game of hide-and-seek with the lively little boy before eventually cornering him behind one of the cupboards.

Sigurd was a handsome child, skinny and very tall for his five years. We were not surprised he was thin as he ate so little, and it was largely due to his fads that the only regular items on the menu were fish pudding, fish-balls and boiled sausages.

Hedvig was my favourite, though her mother was often impatient with her, believing her to be backward – but never "naysty".

The child used to play in my room sometimes while I lolled on the bed, reading. She spent hours contentedly fiddling with the things on my dressing table or making a fuss of me, and her first sentences were in English, to her mother's amusement.

"At least she's learning to speak in some language," Fru Olsen said indulgently.

Her husband took a rosier view of life than his wife. He used to make a point of thanking us for ironing his shirts, and we wondered if he wore them crumpled before we arrived.

He also had a passion for pulling our legs and telling us tall stories.

We soon learned to retaliate, our sneakiest coup being a few helpful words of advice when he told us he was going to preside at an important dinner in Oslo and be host to a VIP lady guest from England.

"After dinner, when you offer her a cigarette, the polite thing to say is, 'Have a fag, hag,' " we said.

He nodded, grateful for our counsel. Later, when we inquired whether he had followed our advice, he told us he had – but as he did not sport a black eye or any discomfiture we were never sure whether we had fooled him or not.

One of his favourite questions to us when we passed within earshot was: "Say, do I look pale today?"

We knew the form. "Very pale" was the required answer, which sent him scurrying off to his brown stoneware bottle of geneva, a Dutch spirit distilled from grain and flavoured with juniper berries, which he preferred to the Norwegian firewater tipple, aquavit. This was his pick-me-up to counteract his imaginary paleness and bring colour to his cheeks.

Herr Olsen's paleness was largely a convenient figment of his imagination. We did wonder, though, how so many of his countrymen managed to stay so pale when the sunshine was often hotter than in England, even in the spring and autumn. We almost got sunstroke more than once, and on June 25th we read that Oslo, sweltering in a heatwave, was the hottest capital in Europe.

We decided the Norwegians must be debilitated – in skin colour only – by their excessive central heating, and we waged continual war against the purveyors of this hothouse atmosphere.

Our opening shot in the battle had landed us in trouble. In a cheap hotel where we spent a night in March we turned the radiators off in our bedroom and were roundly reprimanded next day by the manager, who said we could have wrecked the entire central heating system.

Our attempts to introduce a breath of fresh air into the Olsen household were always thwarted, and we had to suffer until the welcome day in mid-May when, to our relief, the heating was turned off. Until then we were forced to make frequent visits to our bedrooms, where we had switched off the radiators with no ill effect on the system, for a few gulps of cold air. This rejuvenated us sufficiently to carry on with our housework.

The air was much drier than in England, as I found out after hanging a thick pair of wet woollen socks on the line outside on an overcast day in April. In less than an hour they were bone dry. No wonder, I thought, they don't need airing cupboards as we British do.

Herr Olsen escaped quite often from the household hothouse by setting off on hunting trips to the mountains. We never saw him return with any booty, but he and his dogs derived great pleasure from these excursions and his wife, no doubt, felt safe from divorce for a short spell.

One day the two dachshunds, Thomas and Henrik, and Eivind the wire-haired terrier were joined by a newcomer, Don, a lean and lithe grey dog imported from Denmark.

That evening Don suddenly took off like greased lightning, with Alicia in hot pursuit. In her dainty high-heeled shoes she was no match for the huge, streamlined hound, and her efforts at capturing him were hampered by three young lads who were whistling at Don and calling him in the opposite direction.

In the end they took pity on her and coaxed the high-spirited animal back to the house, where he begged the panting Alicia for forgiveness with slobbering licks all over her face. From that moment on the two were great buddies, and Don missed no opportunity to accompany us on our rambles through the forests.

Eivind the wire-haired terrier loved to come walkies with me on his own as the two dachshunds used to gang up on him. One day I was out with him in the woods; he was sniffing about in the undergrowth finding all sorts of interesting smells, I was picking raspberries, mostly for myself to eat there and then, the rest for Alicia later.

Suddenly a tall, lanky man appeared from behind a tree several hundred yards ahead of me. He was flitting about like a giant bat in his dark cape, and for a nasty moment I thought I had strayed into Dracula country. I hid behind a bush and watched him warily as he performed some perplexing rituals – bending down and peering at the ground, scooping things up into a large sack, then prowling about again on his mystery quest.

Briefly I wondered whether he was tracking down truffles, though I had never heard that Norway's forests sprouted these sought-after delicacies, but even from this distance I could see that his finds were too big. I nearly leapt out of my skin when he called out in a thin, piping voice: "Come on, come on! Don't just stand there!"

It was uncanny. Did he have eyes in the back of his head? Was this one of Dracula's attributes? He had not turned round and I was sure he hadn't seen me.

His shrill voice rang out again. "Come on, what are you waiting for? We have a lot to do before it gets dark."

My mouth was dry with fear and I still said nothing. What did this nutter with eyes in the back of his head want with me? And why did he have to get back to his damp dungeon, or wherever he hung out, before dark when his sort normally shunned the daylight?

At last he turned round and beckoned me with a bony finger. Nervously I went towards him, glad I had Eivind with me – though I didn't think he would be much good against a vampire. I now saw that what the stranger was putting into his sack wasn't dead bodies or even dead rabbits. It was stumps of wood and old twisted roots.

I felt a little easier in my mind and plucked up sufficient courage to ask: "What are those bits of wood for?"

"You'll see, you'll see in due course. Now come on, let's get on with it – we're wasting time."

I was ordered to poke about among the fallen pine needles for chunks of old tree root – "but not if they're rotten", he said. "They must be in good condition."

Obediently I did as I was told, and instead of picking and eating raspberries I had to spend the next two hours helping the Master find his old roots. Eventually he had two sacks full and I hoped my ordeal had come to an end. I reckoned without the ghoul of the woods.

"Now, you take this sack and I'll manage the other one," he said. "Follow me."

"Where are we going?" I managed to ask in a

squeaky voice. I was still petrified. If it was to his castle I would somehow have to make my getaway here and now.

"Back to my hut," he said. "I'll show you my carvings."

So that was it! His carvings. Was this the Norwegian equivalent of etchings? Either way, I wasn't keen, but by this time we had reached his little wooden shack in a clearing in the forest. He opened the door and I had to admit the place looked quite welcoming and ordinary inside, apart from the dozens of trolls, monsters and other freakish creatures which were stacked round the walls and in every available space.

Dracula must have seen my look of amazement, for he actually laughed in a croaky way and said: "Didn't I explain? I'm a wood carver and make things out of roots to sell in Oslo. I thought that as you had nothing special to do in the forest you would like to help me."

He took down the biggest, ugliest troll he could find and thrust it into my hands. "Here you are, this is a thank-you for your hard work. Come and see me again if you like."

Clutching my troll, I ran back home, followed by Eivind, to show everyone my booty and recount my strange adventure in the wood. Fru Olsen pounced on my troll.

"That's just what we need – it will make a lovely door stop here in the kitchen," she said. "You can have it back, of course, when you leave."

Alicia added: "And we'll call him Dracula."

4
In Love with Oslo

We fell in love with Oslo, though I secretly wished it were still called Christiania, the name it was given in 1624 by King Christian IV, who rebuilt it on a new site around Akershus Castle after a great fire destroyed the original 11th Century city at the foot of Ekeberg.

Oslo, whose name was restored in 1925, had in 1953 a quiet dignity which had not yet been sacrificed to the commercialism of the Eighties. Even the twin culture shock of nylon tights and ice cream parlours was not to hit the city for another two decades.

The neat rectangular grid of streets in the city centre, many cobbled, perfectly matched the unsophisticated, unostentatious character of the inhabitants. In the town centre in front of the Storting, the Norwegian Parliament, where an ornamental lake and beautiful fountains were in later years to form the city's focal point, there were only open-air cafes. We occasionally relaxed there with a soft drink to bask in the carefree atmosphere which showed that the people of Oslo had put behind them – though not forgotten – the miseries of the German Occupation and settled back into their uniquely Norwegian way of life.

One of our favourite haunts was the main thoroughfare, Karl Johansgate, named after the Swedish king who ruled after the 1814 union with Sweden released Norway from 300 years of Danish sovereignty.

In 1905 Norway again came under the rule of a Dane, but this time by choice. As there were no descendants of the Norwegian royal line, the country by popular vote elected as their king the Danish Prince Carl, who had been married in 1896 at Buckingham Palace Chapel to his English cousin, Princess Maud, in the presence of Queen Victoria.

Despite their centuries of Danish domination, his subjects adored the quiet naval officer with tattooed arms, crowned as King Haakon VII, who had come to them from that country, Danish accent and all, and they welcomed him back rapturously when he returned after his wartime exile in England. Stories were still being told eight years later of his unconventional behaviour in London, where he once escaped from his CID escort and took a 4d bus ride to a famous department store and had tea and biscuits with the manager.

We were well aware that one of the reasons for the tremendous interest in the Coronation of the new British queen was that she was King Haakon's great-niece, and Prince Charles his godson.

If the Danes were popular with the Norwegians it was a different story with the Swedes, who were still bitterly resented for having allowed the Germans to march through their country into Norway. We knew we were adding fuel to the flames of Norwegian animosity when we maliciously passed on a derogatory remark we heard a group of Swedes make outside the royal palace, which they referred to as "a funny little place".

Originally built as a guest residence for the Swedish king but ending up smaller than planned owing to lack of funds, it dominated Karl Johansgate and we thought it a dignified landmark not to be despised by snotty Swedes. We found Oslo the ideal city in almost every respect: not so big that we had to use the excellent public transport to get around; not so small that its attractions would soon pall.

In the shop windows were displayed all manner of

tempting things – fashionable clothes, mouth-watering patisseries, and beautiful silver earrings and brooches enamelled in brilliant colours – and we pressed our noses wistfully against the windows of the knitwear and jewellers' shops like deprived children hungry for treats we could not afford.

It was not only the shops that were well stocked. Oslo was also well stocked with philandering Norwegian men who, we learnt, were dubbed "squareheads" because of the shape of their skulls. We were captivated by their blue eyes and fair hair, and they made it plain they were equally entranced by our dark hair and brown eyes. But we steered clear of those wearing a gold band on the wedding finger of their right hand.

Our suspicion that Norwegian men were far flightier than Englishmen was confirmed when I read an article in a magazine on the theme "We women of Norway must band together to do something about our fickle menfolk".

What measures they planned to take was not clear, but from our observations we felt convinced they would not be effective.

"The men are rather like gaudy butterflies, aren't they?" said Alicia, looking at a group of Norwegians in their colourful pullovers. "Fluttering from flower to flower without a care in the world."

We both agreed we liked butterflies best of all forms of wildlife.

So many Norwegians – men, women and even children – stared at us before we had even opened our mouths that we guessed they had seen few foreigners since the Occupation.

The country had, in fact, been sheltered from foreign influences until the war came to turn their world inside out. Hitler told his occupying troops that the Norwegians were suspicious of strangers, introverted and reserved and warned them to take things calmly and not be too hasty in their dealings with the inhabitants.

A beneficial spin-off of the war years, from our point of view, was the universal welcome we received as Britons. There was no mistaking the warmth of feeling the Norwegians had for the nation which had done so much to restore their freedom after its occupation by a force of 400,000 Germans.

People were still angered by memories of enemy soldiers marching arrogantly on the ramparts of Akershus Castle, looking out over the water as they sang "Wir marschieren gegen England". Tales abounded of secret news-sheets being chewed and swallowed when the Germans raided the premises where they were produced, and of hostages being rounded up on the streets and shot.

Some 40,000 Norwegians were imprisoned and 8,000 deported during the war, and only about half survived. In all, 366 were executed. We were not surprised, therefore, that the three million Norwegians could not forgive the enemy and their own compatriot Quisling for the many atrocities committed on their soil, nor for driving into exile in England their beloved King Haakon and Crown Prince Olav.

Nowhere were the miseries of the Occupation more poignantly depicted that in the dramatic murals in Oslo City Hall. This splendid harbourside building had been officially inaugurated only three years previously, though its foundation stone was laid in 1931, and we visited it on numerous occasions to admire the paintings, sculptures and furnishing by Norway's top artists and craftsmen and the grey and white marble floors, richly embellished in gold, of the spacious halls, galleries and central staircase.

Scenes of the Occupation featured prominently in one of Alf Rolfsen's frescoes: enemy dive-bombers, prisoners lined up before the firing squad, patriots meeting secretly in the cellars below ruined buildings, men silhouetted against the barbed wire of prison camps, and the ultimate liberation symbolised by children processing up towards a still invisible future.

The homecoming of the royal family in 1945 and the liberation of prisoners, with a mother beside a memorial to the fallen, were incorporated in a mural by Henrik Sørensen on the theme of the nation at work and play.

The room which fascinated us most was the east gallery adjoining the City Council chamber. The daily life of the city was the motif of Per Krohg's "beehive" fresco, which portrayed in rich, dark colours the workers busy at their various tasks, entering and leaving the many hive-like buildings.

Another of his frescoes included a symbolic representation of the infamous Grini concentration camp near Oslo, where 19,000 Norwegians were imprisoned. The Germans were shown as giant armoured insects.

Even when we did not go inside, Alicia and I often sat near the imposing courtyard approach to the City Hall and watched the fountain cascade. This was dominated by a resplendent 16ft astronomical clock with five hands, which was floodlit after dark.

The City Hall boasted an even larger clock on its east tower. We were told its 28ft diameter dial was the largest in Europe – "but I don't believe it", said Alicia. "Surely Big Ben must be larger?"

When we checked in an encyclopaedia we found we were wrong. The clockface of Big Ben, originally intended to be 30ft across, was reduced to 22½ft for aesthetic reasons. So Oslo's clock was indeed the largest, and when it was floodlit after dark it was visible far out to sea.

The Norwegians we talked to were very proud of their City Hall and flattered at our genuine praise.

Everyone was happy to chat to us, and kindness and super-kindness were shown to us by young and old.

Families invited us into their homes for meals and girls persuaded their boyfriends to drive us on sightseeing tours of the countryside. One girl we hardly knew sought us out in the youth hostel where we spent our first few days in Oslo – we could not afford to pay eight kroner (40p) each a night for a hotel room – and took us to stay with her and her mother for a week until we found jobs.

They even pressed us to go with them in the summer to Spitsbergen, where the father worked as a mining engineer. We were tempted to accept, but by then had already fallen under Oslo's spell.

We wasted no time trying out our rudimentary Norwegian and found it got us quite a long way, though at first we didn't always understand the answers to our questions. Our first encounter was with a lavatory attendant, who gabbled at us, handed us two enormous keys and demanded 25 øre (just over 1p) each for the privilege of using them to unlock the toilet doors.

I was even more adventurous when I toured the National Gallery while Alicia was on a lunch date with a nifty Norwegian she had picked up at a *varme pølser* (hot sausage) kiosk. A woman started declaiming to me about the morbid paintings by Edvard Munch, Norway's greatest artist, and together we enthused over these mind-bending embodiments of anguish and pessimism as we continued round the gallery together. Comparing notes with Alicia later, I found I had added a number of cultural phrases to my vocabulary while she had gathered in a little store of spicier words.

We needed some of the latter when dealing with the drunken men we saw teetering about even in the mornings. We were amused one day to see a neatly dressed city gent sit down on a park bench, open his briefcase and take out a bottle of aquavit for a quick nip. Another drunk, shabbily dressed and with a matted beard, was skulking behind a tree and made a grab at Alicia in passing. I whacked him in the face with my leather gloves and he slunk off.

Herr Olsen told us later that despite a determined effort over the centuries to curb their age-old lust for drink, the Norwegians always managed to outwit those who legislated to deprive them of their liquor ever since spirits were first introduced into Norway by an archbishop at Trondheim in 1530.

It seemed to us that the various measures and countermeasures in the fight against the demon drink had, over the years, been in as great a state of flux as the Norwegian language, which could never quite decide what form it wanted to take.

The State now had a monopoly of the distribution and sale of wines and spirits, which could not be freely bought as in most other European countries. Despite this, the acquisition of drink, whether for home consumption or in the bar, appeared to be governed by mysterious and random forces which the Norwegians found as perplexing as we did – and these forces certainly failed miserably in vanquishing alcoholism.

We were on surer ground when it came to food, though we quickly realised we would have to adjust our eating habits in Oslo if we were not to starve. Mealtimes were totally haphazard and alien to us, as was the food in the cafes.

As we sampled the unpalatable "hot" dishes, mostly served lukewarm, we thought of the comment of two English travel writers, J. A. Lees and W. J. Clutterbuck, in 1882 that "a general slowness and a fondness for bad food" were the only poor qualities they could detect in the Norwegians.

"I wouldn't agree about the slowness, specially when

it comes to the art of seduction," said Alicia. "But there's no doubt at all about the bad food."

Our biggest mistake was asking for a fried egg, one of the few items on the menu we recognised and felt we would be safe with. It arrived cold, on a slice of bread.

"It must have been among the *smørbrød* on display, but I didn't notice it," Alicia said. "We'd better be more careful in future."

Mostly we did not venture into the cafes, however. Instead, to save money, we sat in the park beside the royal palace to eat cakes or buns. We would have preferred fruit, but there was a poor selection and it was expensive. When we did treat ourselves to a drink in one of the open-air cafes it was usually milk, the cheapest drink on offer and a favourite with Norwegians at breakfast time.

An important aspect of social behaviour was drummed into us when we went into the Grand Cafe, an imposing establishment in the city centre, for morning coffee. Each table was very large, and each was occupied by one woman. As there were no free tables we started asking politely whether "this seat was free". The blunt answer in each case was "No", accompanied by an unfriendly glare. After 10 attempts to find a corner at one of the tables set for six, we got the message: you don't do that sort of thing in Norway.

We quickly got into the Norwegian way of saying "Takk for mat" – thank you for the meal – not only after eating in company but even when getting up from a cafe table, with no one within earshot to appreciate the polite gesture.

Most of our shopping was confined to window gazing, but we did allow ourselves a few luxuries. I bought a beautiful Italian silk scarf for 20 kroner (£1), a hand-knitted Norwegian cardigan with pewter buttons for 120 kroner (£6) and a ski jacket for 60 kroner (£3).

"And before we go back to England I'm going to get one of those down-filled duvets," I said. "They cost 200 kroner but I couldn't face sheets and blankets again."

The Norwegian *dundyner* (duvets) were so cosy and made bed-making so simple that I couldn't understand why they had not found their way into the English shops. They were nothing like the heavy, feather-filled bags I had slept under in Switzerland as the lightweight filling was evenly distributed in 24 gusseted compartments. Most duvets were of duck down, but Fru Olsen's was filled with real eiderdown, which even in Norway, home of the eiderduck, was expensive. She could tell immediately if we switched her duvet by mistake with her husband's.

We never saw double duvets or double beds – "which is surprising considering the Norwegians are so sexy", said Alicia pensively. "They must like to squeeze into a small bed together."

The town boasted some 20 cinemas, which were showing several films in 3D, the newest rage. We enjoyed these but found them tiring on the eyes. Most of the films were in English, but sometimes there was a French film and we caught ourselves reading the Norwegian subtitles instead of listening to the French.

"It's a funny thing about subtitles," I said to Alicia. "I even find myself reading the Norwegian subtitles in the English films."

One of the hottest films to reach the Oslo circuit was *Rashomon*, the Japanese story of murder and rape which had been released the year before. Pornography, for which the Swedes and Danes had such a consuming appetite, was illegal in Norway and if any such sinful material changed hands among the ostensibly more puritanical Norwegians, it was under the counter.

We soon exhausted the highlights of the tourist attractions at Bygdøy, a little way out of the city, where the Kon-Tiki raft, the Viking ships and Nansen's Polar ship *Fram* were housed. We also visited the open-air folk museum to see the old Norwegian log houses and elaborately carved stave churches which had been moved there from different valleys and laid out as a village.

We even sampled a Norwegian church service in Oslo Cathedral and found it an interesting, if unintelligible, experience. We knew that Olav I Tryggvason, a renowned athlete and the most fabled king in Norway's chequered history, had forcibly converted his subjects to Christianity in the 10th Century, a process completed by the first king of all Norway, Olav II Haraldsson, who was canonised after his death.

We also knew that the Lutheran religion was established in Norway at the time of the Reformation in 1536 – "but I had no idea how different the services were from the Church of England", Alicia whispered as we sat in the congregation, wondering when, if ever, we were going to get up and sing hymns.

We decided it was time to venture further afield – a half-hour bus ride out of town – to the Frogner Park with its 192 remarkable sculptures, comprising 650 figures, by Gustav Vigeland on the theme of Man.

I noticed Alicia loitering beside one of the more erotic groups of figures and was about to comment on her new-found interest in the sculptor's technique when I realised her motives were less praiseworthy. Her attention had simply been diverted by two flesh-and-blood males – equally erotic looking but fully clothed, unlike the statues – who slowed down to eye us and the sculptures.

A farcical discussion on the artistic merits of Vigeland's work degenerated into a lively verbal exchange of sexual innuendo and a date for that evening at the restaurant beneath the Holmenkollen ski jump.

"Sounds promising," said Alicia. "It's a good job

we've studied those sculptures so we know what sort of clinches these Nordic types can get into."

We were leaving the Frogner Park through the impressive wrought-iron gates created by Vigeland when we noticed a group of Norwegians pointing at someone near by and tittering. We wondered what they found so funny and realised it was a kilted Scot, destined like all his countrymen to be the butt of Norwegian jokes.

"Tee hee, there's a man in a skirt," guffawed a young man, nearly choking with mirth.

The kilted one swaggered off with swinging gait and swirling skirt, oblivious of the mockery his attire had engendered. We for our part couldn't resist a smile at the sight of the rakish Norwegian "Teddy Boys" who strutted about town wearing royal blue suits – the rather unimaginative equivalent of the flamboyant Edwardian-style outfits sported by many English youths of the day.

"They may swank about as though they're the cat's whiskers in their fancy blue suits, but give me a kilted boyfriend any day," was Alicia's opinion.

5
Thor's Thunderbox

The hills outside Oslo were a popular year-round playground for the Norwegians, who were still jubilant at having foiled a post-war plan for hydroelectric development amid their precious forests. People were also still reminiscing about the Winter Olympics which the town had hosted in 1952.

The highlight of the winter season was Holmenkollen Day in March, when the daring elite launched themselves off the famous ski jump, a prominent landmark jutting out from the forest-clad slopes and one which I could see from my bedroom window far away on the opposite side of the fjord.

This prestigious event had been held every year since 1892 except during the Second World War. The vast crowds who congregated beside and below the dauntingly steep run to watch the contest always included Crown Prince Olav, an accomplished sportsman, who had been a faithful spectator since 1911 and made his debut on the jump in 1922.

Holmenkollen Day was the only time we had seen the smart restaurant tucked in beneath the "launching pad" deserted. Alicia and I sometimes went there on the Holmenkollen railway, which started near the National Theatre in Oslo. At the end of the half-hour journey we enjoyed a snack either in the ski jump cafe or at the restaurant a little way up the line at Frognerseteren, the terminus. From there we could enjoy the fabulous view over the myriad rocky islets which dotted the fjord.

We were on our way up in the train one day when a Norwegian soldier moved into the seat opposite. At once he struck up a conversation and spent most of the journey trying to find out our nationality. Were we Dutch? No? German perhaps? Spanish or Italian? We kept him guessing, and only "British" did not seem to occur to him. After all, the Brits did not speak foreign languages, certainly not Norwegian.

We were laughing to ourselves at his desperation to place us, and as neither of us fancied him we decided to rid ourselves of his insipid company when we reached Frognerseteren. This proved less easy than we anticipated as he stuck to us like a leech and sat down at our table in the cafe, still bent on unravelling the mystery of our origins.

Telling him we were going to "powder our noses", we got up and went to the cloakroom to work out an escape stratagem. Our salvation was close at hand, for a door led directly from the cloakroom on to the hillside.

"Aha," said Alicia. "The Norwegian Army will have to improve its training techniques if it is to outwit us and our evasion tactics."

Not long after this episode, some students who had already befriended us and shown us over the university invited us to join them one April weekend at a students' hut in the forests above the city.

"Sounds like fun," Alicia said to me. "Dozens of frisky, bespectacled students, sleeping bags, log fires and so on. Roughing it, hacking our way through the undergrowth – I fancy myself on a romantic safari."

"Cold safari more like," I said, reminding her that the fjord had barely thawed and horses and carts had only just stopped using it as a short cut. The forests were still half-frozen and there was deep snow higher up in the hills. "So I expect we'll get pneumonia," I added darkly.

"The trouble with you is that you've been brought up soft. You lack the spirit of adventure."

I snorted. "Your idea of adventure is confined to bars and park benches."

Despite my misgivings, however, we joined our new friends one Saturday morning outside the university and set off with them on the train which chugged its way up into the hills.

The next stage of the journey was on foot, through the dense forests in a biting wind. This was the area of Nordmarka, usually covered in snow from mid-December to early April, which offered the people of Oslo skiing on their own doorstep.

The climax of the winter sports season was reached at Easter, when the Norwegians flocked there in their hundreds to ski the forest trails and the slalom and downhill slopes. There were even places where they could practise ski jumping. Those who wanted to stay overnight or longer could find a wide variety of accommodation, from the most basic tourist huts to more sophisticated pensions and hotels.

I was beginning to wish that Alicia and I had thought of trying out a bit of skiing before the snow melted, but I could see we had left it too late as the season was on its last legs and there didn't seem to be any skiing going on. There was quite a bit of snow still lying on the ground, though.

As Alicia walked ahead of me with a ginger-haired student named Gunnar, her dainty shoulders weighed down with an enormous rucksack, I thought she looked ridiculous tramping through the snow furrows in shorts and leather boots. Everyone else, including me, was wearing warm trousers and gumboots, but Alicia had decided these were not feminine enough for her.

Her companion obviously approved of her attire – every time she floundered into a snowdrift he hauled her out and diligently massaged her sodden legs and whatever else he felt appropriate.

"You conniving wretch," I mouthed when I got close enough. "You seem to be treating this as a sex jaunt, not a serious outdoor weekend. I must say you have a wanton outlook on life."

Alicia smiled complacently, wiggled her bottom and slipped fastidiously into another snowdrift. She reached out a helpless hand for Gunnar, who spent five minutes pulling her out and drying her legs. I was so busy spying on her that I put my leg through some snow-covered poles forming a narrow bridge over a stream and got a bootful of icy water. I swore softly. If there was one thing I detested it was getting wet feet at the start of an outing.

I squelched the rest of the way – and the "walk" took five hours.

Even Alicia began to flag. "So this is their idea of a short walk," she whined when nobody was listening.

I told her to stop snivelling, but she persisted: "This is the kind of route march you see on films. I could have joined the army if I needed this sort of torture."

By now I could only grunt breathlessly. When we eventually arrived at the hut we found 50 students from different parts of the world unpacking little parcels of food in the kitchen and unrolling sleeping bags on bunks made of planks of wood.

Alicia stared at the bunks in horror. "We can't sleep on these," she wailed.

Gunnar grinned. "Don't worry, my pretty. You won't notice the hard boards, I promise you."

There was worse to come than the hard bunks. When we inquired the whereabouts of the toilet we were pointed in the direction of an outside shack at the rear of the hut. Inside was a six-seater "thunderbox", its row of companionable but draughty holes jutting into space above the unsavoury products of communal effort heaped up over the years.

Performances were carried out under the fierce gaze of Thor, the god of thunder, who looked down encouragingly from a large painting on the wall as though to bless the Earthmen's puny endeavours. In his hand was his magic hammer, the Norse equivalent of the boomerang, which was said to return to his grasp after he had thrown it. We wondered if this deadly weapon might wham out from the wall to punish those whose products did not come up to the required standard.

On returning to the kitchen we found a scene of hectic activity. Men and women were busily cooking their individual meals. Sausages were sizzling, fishballs steaming, soup simmering and *smørbrød* being decorated. Only then did it dawn on me with appalling certainty that Alicia and I were going to go hungry, for all we had brought with us was a small packet of sandwiches each and a tin of sardines with no can opener. We had forgotten to bring any tea or milk and would have to satisfy our thirst with water from an outside tap.

"So if we don't get pneumonia we'll starve to death," Alicia complained. "Why on earth didn't you think of bringing more to eat?"

I remonstrated: "It's no use scolding me. I thought there'd be a cafe here, but we might have known there wouldn't be such a luxury. Still, if you flutter your eyelashes I expect you'll manage to cadge us a cup of coffee from someone – and make sure you flutter hard enough for us both."

By now everyone else was tucking with gusto into delicious-looking meals, and even the fishballs looked appetising for once to our envious eyes. After supper – a euphemism in our case – we all gathered in a large room where logs were blazing in the corner fireplace. Half a dozen students produced guitars and accordions and a rowdy sing-song started. I sneezed, and a large man put his arm round me protectively.

Alicia realised the excellence of this ploy and sneezed, too. A woman hissed "Sshhh" and gave her a box of paper hankies.

I snuggled closer to my protector to annoy Alicia. I was looking forward to my bed, hard though it was, at about midnight when one of our friends announced that we were all going to take our sleeping-bags into the forest and spend the night beneath the stars – the few that were visible through the dense treetops – in the hope of hearing ptarmigan and wood-grouse at dawn.

"It will be fun," said our friend. "We'll make up mattresses out of twigs and leaves. You'll enjoy it, you really will."

My protector hugged me closer and said slyly: "Yes, indeed you will. I'll look after you. I have an extra large sleeping-bag so you won't need to be all on your own in the cold. We will be nice and snug together."

"In that case I'll come, of course," I wheezed gallantly.

Alicia also decided she was not going to miss the jollity.

"If you can find a cosy berth, so can I," she said. "Gunnar has only a single sleeping-bag, and I'm tired of him, anyway. He almost skinned my legs, he rubbed them so hard on the way here."

Poor Alicia, she never found a sleeping-bag to share. Haggard and numb with cold, she spent the night all alone on a wobbly pile of prickly twigs beneath a snow drift, and no one looked more relieved than she did when it was time for the homeward trek.

"I don't think I like safaris after all," was her disgruntled verdict on our rugged weekend.

We both hoped for cushier fun when we were invited by Helge, one of the students we had met at the hut, to a farewell party he was giving for a friend named Odin, who was going to live in Sweden.

"But Helge means 'saint' so I expect it will be rather a dull 'do'," said Alicia. "Still, nothing ventured, nothing gained."

Helge offered to fetch us by car and arrived in a rickety old Baby Austin. Dressed to kill, we clambered in. There wasn't much room as there were three other men in the car, so we chose the softest knees to sit on in the back seat.

The steering was alarmingly erratic and gave us some anxious moments – and an excuse for our escorts to cuddle us comfortingly. As the car veered wildly down the double hairpin bend on the way out of our village, nearly careering into a patch of gorse beside the road, we clung to them in terror.

Miraculously, we arrived in one piece at Helge's flat, where we were introduced to Odin, the guest of honour. I could see that Alicia was as taken aback as I was. Clearly we had both pictured him in our minds as a bearded hulk modelled on the one-eyed god of war, Odin, who in Norse mythology rode the eight-legged horse Sleipnir and welcomed slain warriors to Valhalla.

Instead, a slender, effeminate creature with silky blond locks stretched out a limp-wristed arm and feebly shook our hands, bidding us welcome in a prissy voice.

"And this is Odin's brother, Bent," said the saintly Helge, blissfully unaware of what we found so comical.

Bent was tall, gaunt and tantalisingly masculine and I thought his parents must have had a warped sense of humour when it came to naming their sons. Alicia and I competed coquettishly for Bent's favours and he thoughtfully shared these between us as we sat on either side of him on the sofa, eating cold sausages and drinking steaming hot chocolate.

We sat chatting with our new friends, who apart

from us and Bent were sprawling on the floor in front of the fire.

Odin monopolised much of the conversation and was continually quoting Ibsen to alert us all to the evils of modern society. The great dramatist's play *Pillars of the Community* was Odin's bible, exposing as it did the "gilded and painted exterior" which concealed society's hollow and corrupt soul.

From what I had seen of Norway so far I was surprised at Ibsen's and Odin's vehemence, as the nation did not seem to me to have been seriously tainted yet by the sins of the western world. But I felt I had to bow to Ibsen's superior insight, even though he was writing about the carryings-on of nearly 80 years ago.

I did not feel on sure enough ground to enter into any arguments with the well-versed Odin on the subject and confined my conversation to provocative banter with his manly brother.

An hour passed and there was no sign of the other guests. More sausages appeared and another hour passed. One of the men played some Norwegian folk tunes on his accordion and another told risqué jokes. Eventually I asked when "the others" were coming.

"Others? What others?" said Helge.

"The other guests."

"Oh, I don't think anyone else is coming," he replied casually, offering me some more sausages.

Alicia and I stirred uneasily, aware that we must look ridiculously overdressed in our glad rags, which we had borrowed from Ingrid. The men, fortunately, gave no indication that they considered this a fault – on the contrary, they made it clear they found us most alluring as they plied us with sausages, songs and flattery.

There was a brief interlude when a girl popped her head round the door, saying she was going to another party.

Discussing the "do" later, Alicia and I didn't know whether to feel honoured that we had been singled out as the only revellers on this sausage-ridden occasion, or whether Helge had turned to us as a last resort.

"All in all, it was almost as big a fiasco as that rotten weekend at the students' hut," said Alicia. "Still, it was better than staying at home washing our hair, I suppose. But I never want to see a cold sausage again."

6
A Spot of Trouble

Alicia brought me the good news one morning in the kitchen.

"Fru Olsen is going to drive us to Sweden for a weekend's shopping. We're all going except Herr Olsen and Hedvig."

We were very excited, and every time he saw us Herr Olsen, who never missed a chance of teasing us, said: "Say, you look very pale today. Have you got travel fever?"

So to please him I got a bit paler and acquired a sore throat, though that was not unusual with the excessive central heating. I told him I had got travel fever, badly.

When the time came to set off on the six-hour drive Alicia, Ingrid, the two older children and I squeezed into the car, with Fru Olsen at the wheel. Our way lay through the mysterious forests of eastern Norway, so dense that people were said to have got lost in them and never been found.

Elsa was nervous at her mother's driving and didn't mind saying so. We were even more nervous but were too polite to show it. As Fru Olsen roared round the bends on two wheels and the wrong side of the road we held our breath and prayed. Somehow we stayed alive.

Half an hour went by and Elsa asked: "Are we in Sweden?" We said no, not for a long time yet. Ten minutes later she repeated her question. After two more tries she got bored and went to sleep. Strangely, we lost our way only five times. As most of the roads had no turnings off them there was not much choice of route – but when we did go wrong, we didn't discover it for miles.

Eventually we reached the Swedish border. Fru Olsen, the children and Ingrid did not have to leave the car as they needed no passports, but Fru Olsen came in with us to supervise our passage through Customs.

Alicia and I had to fill in forms and I watched her to see what to put as I wasn't feeling too well. When I handed in my form to the cynical blond official, I thought something looked slightly amiss. For a moment I couldn't place what it was. Then I realised. I had put Alicia's surname instead of my own.

Blushing in shame, I asked for the form back, crossed out her name and put my own. The Swede looked at me coldly.

On the other side of the border post we got into the car again and set off along the neat and tidy roads of Sweden, so different from the rugged landscape of Norway which we had just left behind.

Elsa had mixed feelings when Fru Olsen suggested that as the Swedes drove on the left-hand side of the road Alicia, who had a British driving licence, might like to drive the Mercedes for a while. The child quickly realised that my friend's nonchalant handling of the vehicle was a blessing after her mother's wildness at the wheel.

When we reached our destination, Gothenburg, we all had to fill in forms at the hotel reception. At first we were disconcerted because the woman behind the desk was looking at us as she spoke but calling us "she". Fru Olsen explained that this was merely Swedish formality, using "he" or "she" in place of "you".

"How very droll," Alicia said as we filled in the forms.

For "occupation" I put "housemaid", Alicia put "secretary" and Ingrid "nanny". The receptionist looked at Fru Olsen with respect. Even in Sweden not everyone travelled with secretary, nanny and housemaid.

There was only time for a meal and bed, so we did that. Next morning I woke up with spots. We didn't notice them until after lunch, though earlier Alicia told me I looked more peculiar than usual.

During the morning we went on a shopping spree. Fru Olsen wanted to buy three silk dresses – they cost about 200 Swedish kronor (£10) each as silk was much cheaper than in Norway – and a lot of clothes for the children, but the Norwegian travel allowance wouldn't stretch that far. Grumbling, she had to content herself with fewer purchases, which included small lace hankies for Alicia and me. Ingrid bought a swimsuit, four pairs of earrings and a glass pig.

We had lunch in a place where Fru Olsen thought the tablecloth was "rather naysty". She made the waitress change it, and then she thought the food was rather nasty, too. We tried to pretend we didn't belong with her.

Suddenly she looked at me and said: "Have you got a fever? You look pale and your eyes are rather bright."

Everyone felt my throbbing forehead and decided I had measles. Fru Olsen asked: "Would you like to go to bed or come with us to the funfair?"

As I had spent what little money I had brought with me I decided on bed. In any case, I didn't really feel up to whirling about on roundabouts.

I was whisked secretly into the hotel and sent to bed with a warning from Fru Olsen to be sure no one found out what was wrong with me as they were very strict in Sweden and would have isolated me in hospital. As none of us had much money left this would have been awkward.

Fru Olsen drew the curtains and lent me her dark glasses in case I went blind with the measles. When a steward brought up a tray of tea during the afternoon I tried not to look too spotty and he went away saturated with germs and destined for the isolation hospital.

In the evening the others came to look at me.

"We've had a lovely time," said Fru Olsen cheerfully. "What a pity you decided not to come. We went on the giant dipper and supersonic roundabout, and Elsa lost her shoe coming down the helter-skelter."

She was keen to go on to Copenhagen – Denmark was a favourite shopping place for the Norwegians – but was dissuaded when we pointed out that her husband might not like her to be away so long. Besides, I might need medical attention. So in the morning I was hidden in my overcoat and dark glasses and slid into the car before the hotel porters could even say "Good morning". No one had time to examine my throat or take my pulse and isolate me.

Only one barrier lay between me and freedom – the dreaded blond Swede at the Customs post. With my collar turned up and my dark glasses sinister in the sunless light, I signed the forms with difficulty as I had to keep my gloves on to hide my spotty hands.

The blond eyed me with distaste but failed to penetrate my disguise. I slipped out of the Customs shed, but only just in time. Another official, astuter than the first, appeared from round the corner, eyed me suspiciously and whispered to his colleague. They came hurrying towards me.

"Come back!" they yelled. "We want to ask you some questions."

But Fru Olsen was at the ready, crouched over the wheel of the car. Alicia held the door open, I leapt in and the car shot away. The two Swedes were left far behind, waving their arms and shouting. Whether they had noticed my spots or whether I had again filled in the wrong name on my form I shall never know.

Thus it was that I escaped into Norway to have my

measles in peace. Only they turned out to be scarlet fever.

I had to take to my bed, much to Alicia's disgust, for she had to do all my work as well as her own and even had to help Fru Olsen clean my room before the doctor came. Herr Olsen was very smug as he had joined us to the Norwegian health service just before the Swedish trip and did not have to pay the doctor's fees.

It wasn't that he had second sight – his warnings about travel fever were only his idea of fun – but he admitted he didn't trust his wife's driving and anticipated we would all end up in hospital with broken bones.

The doctor arrived during the morning and was shown up to my room. He looked at my spots, peered into my throat, felt the glands in my neck, took my temperature and pulse, and finally examined the soles of my feet with the utmost care.

I wondered what my feet had to do with it and decided that the doctor must be looking to see if my skin was peeling from the extremities up. This was pure conjecture on my part as I had never come across anyone who had suffered from scarlet fever, and the elderly doctor was of the old school and not inclined to discuss my illness.

After satisfying himself that I did indeed have *skarlagensfeber*, the doctor prescribed penicillin and ordered me to stay in bed. When I told him Fru Olsen assumed I had measles – which I thought unlikely since I had already had them at the age of two – he unbent so far as to concede that in past centuries the medical profession had often confused these two infectious diseases.

If scarlet fever was as infectious as I was led to believe, why, I asked myself, was no one else in the household showing signs of catching it from me? We had all been squeezed in the car together and they had ample opportunity to breathe in my germs. And why had none of my family or childhood friends had the illness?

I pondered all this as I languished in bed, and I made the best of my misfortune and used my enforced idleness for cultural advancement. I read, in Norwegian, *Three Men in a Boat* and *Lady Chatterley's Lover*, which I had bought in Oslo, and listened to broadcasts in English from Moscow and Warsaw on the radio which Alicia had lent me with a bad grace.

It was the first time I had heard broadcasts from behind the Iron Curtain, and one night I heard the Kremlin clock strike midnight.

My enjoyment of my illness was marred only by the fact that I missed the fun of National Day on May 17, when there were celebrations throughout the country to mark Norway's independence in 1814. Britain's Princess Margaret was to be among the guests, and Fru Olsen asked Alicia if she would like to borrow the Mercedes to drive to the airport and see the English Princess arrive. When we read later about the severe congestion on the roads to the airport, Alicia was glad she had refused the offer.

As for the town, it had gone quite mad, she told me that evening as she regaled me with the day's happenings. Everyone was in what they termed *perlehumør* (pearl humour), singing, chanting and fervently waving the Norwegian flag. We had long since voted this second only in splendour to the Union Flag and had noticed it sneaking into fetes and festive occasions in England and getting itself hoisted in preference to other national flags.

Girls in national costume and students wearing red or blue uniforms – the colour depended on which type of high school they had graduated from – marched proudly through the city with their school bands. Other students in weird costumes drove through the streets in old jalopies painted bright red to mark the start of a rag lasting several weeks. Another of their pranks was to take breakfast in bed to their teachers, and the following day there was a picture in the newspaper of a headmaster being greeted in bed by three lovely damsels.

Princess Margaret joined King Haakon and his family on the balcony of the royal palace at the far end of Karl Johansgate to acknowledge the cheers of the exuberant crowd and wave to the thousands of children.

Alicia, for her part, entered into the spirit of the festivities with redoubled zest – "to make up for your absence", she explained – though she said she had found the boisterous bands and rejoicing processions overawing. Someone warned her she might have to stand for two hours to see the children pass and she reluctantly admitted to me, under my persistent interrogation, that she had shunned the hurly-burly of the city and sought instead the solitude of a fjordside cove to celebrate in her own unique style – with a young Finn on a visit to Oslo.

While she was having fun with her Finn, I had been frittering away some of the long hours on my sickbed scouring the papers for news of a scarlet fever epidemic. I was aware that if the disease really was highly infectious I may well have spread my germs to all four corners of the globe.

The only titbit of news was brought home by Alicia, who reported that the students' hut we had stayed in had been closed down and fumigated after a virulent outbreak of the disease.

7
Follow my Leader

June 2nd in the Olsen household and all over Norway was a red letter day. Everywhere the media buzzed with excitement as it relayed news of the Coronation in Westminster Abbey of Queen Elizabeth II, great-niece of Norway's King Haakon.

The Coronation hit the front page headlines in the Norwegian newspapers, and Alicia and I wallowed in reflected glory as we all spent most of the day listening to the broadcasts from London and Oslo. Two radios were going, one in the dining-room, where Alicia and I listened to the English service, the other in the kitchen, where the rest of the family tuned in to the Norwegian broadcast.

The reception from Oslo was much clearer, so whenever no commentary was broadcast Alicia and I dashed back into the kitchen to hear the music from Westminster Abbey.

Not much housework was done that day, and *middag* was even more meagre than usual.

News of the conquest of Everest on May 29 – a feat succinctly summed up in Sherpa Tensing's immortal words "We done the bugger!" – shared the front pages of the Norwegian papers with the British queen and made it a day to remember.

Another item of interest to us was that Gordon Richards had become the first jockey to be knighted, though we had been even more thrilled a few weeks previously to learn that Winston Churchill, whose rousing speeches had echoed in our young hearts during the war, had been made a Knight Commander of the Garter.

The Coronation film arrived in Oslo in record time. The cinema was packed and the huge audience, enthralled, gasped in wonder as the majestic golden coach, the three cherubs on its roof supporting a model of the Imperial State Crown, came into view carrying the dark-haired young queen and her Consort.

The spirit of jubilation among the crowds in London, in no way diminished by the rainy weather, was quickly communicated to this cinema audience far across the sea. If Britain had not witnessed such scenes of pageantry for 16 years, since King George VI was crowned, Norway had seen nothing like it since 1906, when their own King Haakon VII was crowned in Trondheim.

"Britain, of course, is better than any other country at organising this sort of pomp and glory," said Alicia, her voice tinged with pride as we watched the Queen's Trumpeters, the Brigade of Guards, the Household Cavalry and the Yeomen of the Guard, who formed only part of the queen's 12,000-strong escort.

A Norwegian woman sitting next to me had heard what Alicia said and whispered to me: "Yes, and do you know, we won't ever be having a Coronation in Norway again. It has been decided to dispense with the ceremony in future. I am so sad, and also very envious of your British love of pageantry. I only wish I could have gone to London for the Coronation – my children are over there and will be bringing back photographs to show me."

While she was talking there was a frisson of excitement in the audience as the Queen Mother and Princess Margaret passed across the screen in the Irish State Coach. And when the newly honoured Winston Churchill, in his robes as a Knight of the Garter, came into view there was loud applause for the adored wartime leader whose stirring words, heard by Norwegian patriots on secret radios, had kept their spirits high in the dark days of the Occupation.

There was a hushed silence as the scene moved into Westminster Abbey, where every Coronation had taken place since William the Conqueror came to claim the English throne in 1066.

"Did you know that he was crowned on Christmas Day?" I asked the Norwegian woman. "It was the second Coronation that year as King Harold II had been crowned in the January. Poor old Harold defeated and killed one of your invading kings, Hardraade of Norway, only to get a Norman arrow in the eye at the Battle of Hastings three days later."

The woman seemed genuinely interested in this snippet of potted history which I had fed her while the clergy, nobles, Kings of Arms, heralds and other dignitaries who were among the 7,000 people in the congregation were processing into the abbey.

The Norwegian audience were plainly awed by the solemnity of the rites involved in the anointing and crowning of the 27-year-old queen on King Edward's Chair, where British monarchs before her had been crowned over the centuries. And they marvelled at her regal composure as she sat wearing the heavy St Edward's Crown, which was made for Charles II in 1661 because the ancient crown and regalia had been destroyed by the Parliamentarians after the execution of King Charles I.

"What a lovely young queen," a voice was heard to say from the back of the cinema. "And isn't that little Prince Charles in the gallery, watching his mother being crowned?"

"Ssshhh!" said someone as the monarch was symbolically lifted on to her throne to receive the homage of her subjects. "We'll crown you if you talk so loud – we'll miss what is happening."

Not a sound came from the audience after that as the ceremony came to its close and the new queen, now wearing the less weighty Imperial State Crown and purple velvet Robe of State, led the fine company out of the abbey to return triumphantly to her palace.

We and all the Norwegians felt we had really had our money's worth – "It was almost as good as being there", I heard an old lady say.

"Better, probably," said her husband. "You wouldn't have seen as much if you had spent all those tiring hours standing by the roadside like those other poor people. We have seen it all in comfort, and I certainly will never forget this wonderful film."

As members of the British colony in Oslo, Alicia and I were invited to a special reception at the Ambassador's residence on the evening of June 2nd. The invitation stated that in the event of bad weather, the function would be postponed for two days as it was to be held in the garden.

It did, of course, pour with rain, so we stayed at home. Next day we read in the newspapers that the reception had taken place after all, complete with fireworks and pageantry. We were furious.

Alicia glowered. "Just look at all that party food we've missed," she said, pointing to a photograph in the paper of the Ambassador cutting a magnificent many-tiered cake.

"I hope they all had soggy *smørbrød* and watery wine."

We had to console ourselves with the prospect of the Coronation Ball at the British Embassy three days later. This we did not miss, though the event posed some problems over what we should wear. Alicia was expecting a clothes parcel from home to supplement the few winter garments she had brought with her. I, too, had only warm woollies.

"So we won't exactly look glamorous, will we?" I said petulantly. "We'll just have to miss that knees-up, too."

Fru Olsen was determined that lack of suitable attire should not prevent our attending the ball, so she insisted that we try on a selection of her evening dresses. As she was half a head taller than us her skirts dragged on the floor, but after cunning use of Herr Olsen's crimson cummerbund and some adroit work with needle and thread we were eventually sent on our way, with heads held high and skirts hitched precariously, to join our more fashionably clad fellow countrymen.

We swept grandly into the ballroom and made up for being cheated out of the reception by eating twice as much as everyone else. That, however, was the extent of our fun as the guests consisted only of staid British couples and no one asked us to dance.

"What a pity we couldn't have brought a couple of sprightly Norwegians with us to enliven the proceedings," said Alicia ruefully. "Then there would have been high jinks!"

A more minor but closer-to-home royal occasion the previous month – the wedding of Princess Ragnhild, King Haakon's granddaughter, to wartime resistance leader Erling Lorentzen, son of a shipping magnate – prompted Fru Olsen to give us the day off.

"And I'll drive you to watch the procession," she said.

As soon as we reached the centre of Oslo we began to wish we hadn't come. Fru Olsen driving in ordinary traffic was a fearsome experience. Fru Olsen driving in an Oslo gone mad was a nightmare. There was a stationary queue of vehicles more than a mile long in Drammensveien, the main road leading out of town. But

Fru Olsen didn't like waiting, so she turned out of the line of traffic and drove for three-quarters of a mile on the wrong side of the road. As there was room for only three lines of traffic – the middle line being trams – we knew the crunch, probably a literal one, was bound to come as soon as a car and tram came in opposite directions at the same time.

Somehow she got away with her manoeuvre and turned down a side road, having effected a monstrous queue-jump that would have got her lynched in England. And nobody seemed to mind. No one even honked. Surprisingly we arrived safely at Asker, the small village some miles out of Oslo where the wedding ceremony was taking place at the small church. After going round in circles for a while in an effort to outwit the police and elude their parking regulations we were finally forced into an authorised car park. Even Fru Olsen couldn't persuade the police to let us have a special vantage point of our own.

We found a vacant piece of roadside and lined it. Everyone else had flags so we took off our silk scarves and waved those instead. After half an hour there was the sort of stir which seeps through a crowd when IT is going to happen at last. Suddenly an open buggy drove past and everyone cheered. Princess Ragnhild and her husband waved to the crowd – and that was that. The other royal guests, who included the king, Crown Prince Olav and his teenage son Harald, the first Norwegian prince to be born in Norway since 1370, had left the church by another route.

The sight of Norwegian royalty was not new to us as we had seen most of them out and about in Oslo among the ordinary citizens. I recognised Crown Prince Olav once when he got on a tram behind me. And we had several times spotted the 6ft 4in king, the tallest – and at 81 also the oldest – reigning monarch in Europe, in the spacious 1928 Lincoln car he favoured because it allowed him to sit upright in his top hat.

After the newly-weds had passed we found our car, but it took 20 minutes as Fru Olsen had forgotten where she left it. We eased our way into the traffic flow and a little way out of the village we came to a diversion. A large red arrow pointed off the main road so we followed its direction, taking the only road. Five cars followed us.

The road got narrower – and narrower still. By now there were seven cars, two lorries and a bus in our wake. We drove on along the winding road, but as there were no roads branching off it we didn't worry. Nor, it seemed, did our retinue.

As we went on we began to think it a bit odd. The road got less and less like a road and more and more like a forest track. The cars, lorries and bus still tagged on trustingly. Fru Olsen was undaunted but even she thought it queer when the path dipped down into a forest clearing over bumps and brambles. But eager for adventure as usual, she obstinately refused to turn back, even if she could have done with our followers so close behind.

"Perhaps we can get home through the forest," she said. "What fun!"

We began to get embarrassed at the thought of our hangers-on having to get home through the forest, too. Suddenly we came to a narrow opening on the right. It was the only possible way, so Fru Olsen drove in. We found ourselves in a back garden. A tall thin man holding a hoe watched in disbelief as Fru Olsen turned the car on his lawn and drove out again. One by one the other vehicles waited their turn and did the same, the big red bus making the final turn with some difficulty.

And all the time the man with the hoe just stood there speechless with his mouth open. Not one of the drivers looked concerned at the detour, least of all Fru Olsen. Calmly she drove back the way we had come, and calmly the others followed.

At last we got home the proper way, not through the forest, to our relief and Fru Olsen's disappointment. Alicia and I had guilty visions for the rest of the day of the crestfallen man with the hoe, last seen attempting to smooth out the deep ruts in his back lawn.

The Norwegian royal wedding and the British Coronation brought in their wake a little flurry of activity in our neighbourhood, where a group of amateur actors put their heads together and planned a royal revel of their own.

"They are going to stage one of Shakespeare's plays, *Hamlet*," Fru Olsen told us one morning. "As it is about the king of Denmark, and it has a Norwegian in it at the end, they think it will be a very suitable choice. They are going to put the play on in the community hall."

Alicia and I thought it would be a lot of fun to see a cast of Norwegians sing-songing their way through Shakespeare's immortal blank verse.

"I wonder who's going to play Hamlet?" I said.

I soon found out. Less than half an hour later there was a knock at the kitchen door. I went to open it, and there stood a magnificent young man, the very embodiment of a Viking warrior, I thought, but without the horns. He turned his cornflower blue eyes inquiringly on me and asked who I was. I had only got out three words when he interrupted me: "You must be one of the English girls."

I felt piqued that he had seen through my imperfect accent so quickly, but I asked him into the kitchen and said I would fetch Fru Olsen.

"No, don't do that," he said quickly, putting a restraining hand on my arm. "It's you I have come to see."

"Me?" I was flabbergasted. "Why do you want to see me?"

I was, of course, always delighted when a handsome young man expressed a desire for my company, but out of the blue like this? I was suspicious.

"Don't look so anxious," he said, patting my hand. "I've come to ask your help."

By now Alicia, Ingrid and Fru Olsen had come into the room to find out what was going on. Alicia gazed up at the newcomer in undisguised admiration.

The young Adonis explained to Fru Olsen: "Some friends and I are putting on one of Shakespeare's plays to mark the British Coronation, and we heard you had two English girls working here, so we wondered if we might ask them to help."

Fru Olsen was overjoyed at this unexpected intrusion into our sober domestic routine.

"Of course the girls can help," she told him. "They have every evening free, and if they need extra time off they shall have it. You would like that, girls, wouldn't you?"

We didn't hesitate. Alicia spoke for both of us when she said eagerly: "We'd love it. But what do you want us to do? Are we to have big parts? I've never been on stage before, though."

"Nor have I," I added. "But we'll do our best."

Our visitor told us his name was Magnus – Magnificent Magnus, Alicia whispered to me – and suggested we should meet him and the others in his group at the community hall next evening.

"That will be fun, won't it?" said Fru Olsen approvingly, looking at us.

"We certainly hope so," we said together.

We had mixed feelings when we learned next evening what our involvement was to be in this ambitious production. Alicia was cock-a-hoop. She was invited to play

Ophelia – "and as she goes off her rocker it will suit you very well", I muttered venomously. I was marked down for the most humdrum of the backstage chores: coaching Hamlet in his English pronunciation.

"And is there no part for me in the play?" I asked in high dudgeon.

Magnus fondled my neck and said: "Your part will be crucial, so crucial that you really wouldn't have time for anything on stage. All your efforts will be devoted to me, making sure I give my best performance."

The significance of his words was not lost on me, nor on Alicia, for she said: "Perhaps, on second thoughts, I could be the one to do the coaching and she can play Ophelia."

"No, it's all settled," said Magnus. "You are Ophelia – you are made for the part. Now let's get on and start rehearsing or we'll never be ready in time." He added to me: "And if you feel I need some help with my diction we will go back to my place later."

The rehearsal went along at a cracking pace as the cast were all proficient in English, though their sing-song intonation made them sound more like Welsh speakers. I was convinced it would be a waste of time to attempt to eliminate this flaw, so I interrupted only when a serious error of pronunciation was made.

It was not until they came to the scene in Act I where Hamlet learns that his uncle murdered the king that I began to have grave misgivings.

Magnificent Magnus was on stage declaiming about the man who had grabbed the throne after murdering the king and marrying the queen, Hamlet's mother. His words echoed round the little hall:

"O most pernicious woman!

"O willain, willain, smiling, damned willain!

"My tables, my tables, – meet it is I set it down,

"That one may smile, and smile, and be a willain."

I raised my hand and stopped his flow of rhetoric. "Just a moment, Magnus, there's something I have to tell you."

Patiently I explained to him, and the rest of the cast, that an English "v" was pronounced in exactly the same way as a Norwegian "v".

"Ah, yes, of course," said Magnus. "I'll do it again."

After four more tries he got it right, and we were off and away. A little later in the same scene we came to "There's ne'er a willain dwelling in all Denmark . . ." and again, in Act II:

"Bloody, bawdy willain!

"Remorseless, treacherous, lecherous, kindless willain!

"O, wengeance!"

Why, oh why, did they have to choose this particular play, which must surely have more closely packed "villains" in it than any other Shakespeare drama? We still had a number of other "v" hurdles to leap, including "wisitation" and "wacancy" in Act II, and Magnus and his fellow actors all tried hard to avoid falling into this trap.

After this first rehearsal Magnus came up to me and gave me a quick hug of appreciation. "I don't know how we would have managed without you," he said. "And your friend is going to be a lovely Ophelia."

Alicia had certainly enjoyed her role and began to put on airs and graces.

"I wonder if I've missed my true vocation," she said when we got home.

Fru Olsen asked how the rehearsal had gone and we told her we thought the play was going to be a great success as long as the actors could remember to say their "v" sounds properly.

Fru Olsen, although she spoke English fluently, was not sure what I meant.

"Surely it is easy enough for them?" she said. "Anyone can say 'willain', can't they?"

For the umpteenth time I pondered this linguistic enigma. Fru Olsen had failed me. Not only was she unable to explain why Norwegians could not say an initial "v" in English when so many of their own words, including *vi* (we), started with this letter; she could not even understand what I was rabbiting on about.

Rehearsals progressed well, and Magnus asked me to go back with him to his house afterwards to work on his "v" problem. Alicia wasn't too jealous of my close ties with the leading man as the actor who was taking the part of Fortinbras of Norway was paying her plenty of attention.

"And as he has only a few lines to say at the end, he has lots of spare time on his hands," she said. "As soon as I've drowned in the muddy brook we are able to skive off for a couple of scenes."

"I noticed you both vanishing into the wardrobe closet," I said. "I wondered what you were up to. I thought you were trying some of the costumes on."

"It was he who was trying it on," she said. I nodded sagely.

My coaching sessions with Magnus lasted two weeks and things were progressing nicely. We practised all sorts of "v" words, with actions to match, and I felt our get-togethers had been most fruitful and instructive.

The great night came when Shakespeare's masterpiece was to be staged in all its glory. The community hall was packed, and Herr and Fru Olsen, Ingrid, an unwilling Elsa and three willing workmen from the house were among the audience, as well as a sprinkling of the English corps in Oslo, who had received special invitations.

We all sat in places of honour in the front row and I had a copy of *Hamlet* open on my knee in case any of the cast forgot their lines. There was a tense silence as the play opened, and enthusiastic applause between the scenes. Everything went well, no one forgot their lines, Alicia gave a heart-rending performance as Ophelia, and the ghost of the murdered king was a big hit.

"You must have worked very hard with Magnus – he's speaking his part beautifully," whispered Fru Olsen.

Hamlet was in fine fettle as he castigated his wicked uncle.

"O willain, willain, smiling, damned willain!" he bellowed.

The audience loved it and had to be restrained from applauding.

"You see," said Fru Olsen. "I told you there was nothing to worry about. He didn't have any problems with 'willain' after all. But I don't think this *Hamlet* will quite make Oslo's National Theatre."

The evenings were now still light at 10.30pm and it was broad daylight again by 2am. On Midsummer's Eve it was possible to read all night without switching on the light and we found we needed very little sleep. Herr Olsen decided we should not miss the midsummer festivities in Oslo, where one and all flocked to the beaches, hills or countryside in the evening. All one could see were sitting, swimming, walking, riding, driving and boating Norwegians.

We were surprised to learn that Midsummer's Eve – June 23 in Norway – was not a public holiday, as the Norwegians seemed to have far more of these than the British. Their favourite way of celebrating midsummer was out on the water. The fleet of small boats was decked with greenery, while on the shore there were fireworks displays and dancing round giant bonfires.

Herr Olsen arranged for us to have a trip on a motor boat at midnight. As usual he had neglected to take any action until the last minute, and we never found out what strings he had to pull to obtain the much sought-after tickets at such a late stage.

Out on the fjord we had a superb view of the fireworks on land – and a narrow escape from an explosive encounter with two drunken Norwegian men who let off some squibs beneath the seat where we were sitting and nearly capsized the boat while attempting amorous advances during the general panic.

When we eventually reached shore, dishevelled but otherwise unscathed, we made our way to the home of Herr Olsen's mother, where we had stayed on the night of the Coronation Ball. By now it was 3am, and although it was as light as day we fell asleep immediately, exhausted by our first Norwegian-style midsummer romp.

After our Midsummer's Eve excursion on the fjord Alicia and I decided it was time to find out more about the little islands and skerries which we had often viewed from the heights of Holmenkollen.

"I wonder whether we can take a trip to some of them," I said one weekend. "They look uninhabited but it would be fun to explore them. As we have a few days off, now would be a good time to do it."

We inquired at all the likely information points in the city, but no one could tell us how we could reach the islands. Yet we were sure we had seen some small launches speeding towards one of them, and eventually we found a landing stage a little way along the fjordside where we were told that a motor boat plied regularly between some of the islets.

"And you are just in time for the next trip," said the old boatman. "You hop in and I'll take you to that big island in the middle of the fjord. The last boat back is at six o'clock, so make sure you don't miss it or you'll be stranded."

The "big" island was, in fact, a grassy holm with

nothing and nobody on it except a few rabbits. The day was warm and sunny and it made a pleasant change to have our own little haven of peace and quiet to explore – "unmolested by men", as Alicia said priggishly.

What has come over her? I thought. A man in tow was normally as necessary to her sense of well-being as the air she breathed.

The islet was a mile or so long and half a mile wide. At the far end a small clump of stunted trees clung tenaciously to the rocks which fringed the stony shore, and we were pleased to see that even here wild raspberries were growing in abundance in the patches of soil between the boulders.

We stripped down to our skimpy swimsuits and settled down on a bed of soft grass to eat our picnic lunches, watching a family of ducklings drift past. The fish in the clear water darting this way and that like streaks of quicksilver among the dark pebbles had a hypnotic effect on us both.

"What a heavenly place," said Alicia drowsily. "I think I'll stay here for ever like one of Homer's Lotus Eaters."

"I don't think they settled on an island as small as this," I said. "Our lives of idleness would be short-lived because we'd starve before long. They probably had more things than lotus fruit to eat – we have only raspberries."

Our sporadic talk tailed off as the warm sun soaked into us, lulling us into a state of torpor. Soon we were both fast asleep.

It was three hours later when I was awoken by the sound of a bee buzzing near my ear as it danced about in a sprig of wild flowers.

It was still warm, and I closed my eyes again and lay quietly for a while, revelling in the solitude of our tiny kingdom.

Alicia opened an eye and said lazily: "What's the time? I'm hungry?"

I looked at my watch and sprang to my feet. "It's six o'clock," I gasped. "We must have missed the boat."

"Don't be silly, it can't be that late. We've only been sleeping for about half an hour," said Alicia. "Your watch must be wrong."

"Of course it isn't. And look at the sun – you can see it's late afternoon."

We threw on our clothes and ran as fast as we could to the other end of the island where we had come ashore. A motor launch was halfway to the mainland and fast shrinking to a dot.

"So now what are we going to do? We'll probably not survive the night here with no food and shelter," wailed Alicia. "Whose hare-brained idea was it to come out to this God-forsaken island, anyway?"

"Don't blame me, we both thought of it," I said angrily. "And it won't help for us to fall out. We must find ourselves some food and somewhere to sleep."

Supper was easy – we had the raspberries. Shelter was more of a problem as there was not even a tumble-down shed on the island.

"So we'll have to use our ingenuity," I said. "Weren't you ever a Girl Guide or anything useful like that?"

Looking at Alicia, I knew that was not her scene, nor ever would have been. The nearest she had got to Guiding was making a Promise, but only the sort which led to a date, not a Good Deed.

She was still dithering about what we should do, so I scoured the island for a likely resting place for the night. I was just about to tear some bullrushes from the water's edge, with a view to drying them in the sun so that we could use them for bedding, when Alicia gave an excited shout.

I ran across to where she was standing on one of the

high boulders. She was waving her arms wildly and yelling so loudly that I thought she would damage her lungs.

"Look, there's a rowing boat," she said. "Come on, help me attract its attention."

We took off our brightly coloured trousers and flapped them in the air, whistling and bellowing in a most unladylike fashion. Our efforts paid off, for the man in the rowing boat caught sight of us and changed course. By the time he had reached the island we had put our trousers on again – he seemed disappointed to see this – and gathered up our few belongings in readiness for our return to civilisation.

The man in the rowing boat looked at us quizzically. "This is a rum do," he said. "How come you are here all alone at this time of day?"

We explained that we had fallen asleep and missed the last boat home, and he laughed.

"So it's very lucky that I came along," he said, his eyes flashing.

"Yes, very lucky indeed," we said in unison. "And we are very grateful."

"Good," he said. "When we get back we'll pick up my friend Johan and we'll all celebrate your escape from this miniature Alcatraz."

8
What a Carry On!

Since Herr Olsen paid our bus fares into Oslo on our days off we went there often. We soon discovered that the tree-lined avenue leading to the palace was a fruitful starting point for chance encounters. We went there often to sit on the benches beneath the stately trees and watch the dashing Norwegians strolling past. Our glances were returned with interest, and whenever we spotted a particularly dishy specimen we mentally willed him to come and sit beside us – which never failed to lead to a rewarding episode.

One such flirtatious acquaintance was a debonair man who told us he was a technical consultant at the Norwegian broadcasting centre and invited us on a tour of the establishment.

"You will find it very instructive," he assured us in a fruity voice.

"I am sure we will," replied Alicia, giving him a devastating flutter of her eyelashes. He edged closer to her on the bench.

Determined not to be outmanoeuvred, I said: "Do you have soundproof studios and so on?"

He inched in my direction. "Very soundproof, my dear."

I threw a triumphant look at Alicia as he took my hand confidentially.

"And it's very difficult for me to get permission to take visitors round every part of the building, so I hope you'll be grateful for the chance," he said.

A pregnant silence followed, then Alicia said coyly: "Oh, indeed, very grateful."

"Yes, very," I added with my most winsome smile.

We were genuinely grateful for the chance to see round the place as some student friends had already tried without success to fix a visit. Our appointment with our irrepressible new friend Rolf at the broadcasting centre was fixed for the following day as he was shortly leaving for America to research the possibility of bringing television to Norway – at that time only a future dream owing to problems with the mountainous terrain.

Our guide turned out to be in fine form. First he introduced us to the recording studios. In turn we sat in a soundproof booth in front of a microphone, and while we were reading phoney news items or announcing a fictitious programme our host made rapid but ardent passes at whichever of us was with him on the other side of the glass door.

While Alicia was singing a song during her session at the mike, a well-known Norwegian pianist dashed through on his way to give a broadcast in an adjoining studio. He paused long enough to sit at the piano and accompany Alicia for a verse or two before blowing her a kiss and rushing off to his recital.

Our antics at the microphone were followed by an excursion into another studio, where roguish Rolf entertained us by switching off the lights and chasing us round the room in the dark. Our sport, which was enlivened by sudden squeals from Alicia, lasted for a frivolous half-hour or so, then we all agreed to call it a day.

"And what a day!" sighed Alicia as we sat in our favourite cafe munching *smørbrød* and discussing our new heartthrob's invitation to repeat the visit the following day if we were at a loose end.

"And we're very likely to have a loose end if we run riot there again," I remarked.

"Yes," Alicia agreed. "I think I'll go back again tomorrow. That's the kind of game I enjoy playing."

"You wouldn't be safe in those soundproof studios. You might never be heard of again," I cautioned her.

To my surprise she took my advice to heart and did not mention Rolf again. We chatted about other things, but our conversation tailed off as we became aware of a row of blue eyes gazing at us from a nearby table. Five minutes passed and the owner of one pair of eyes got up and moved across to our table. He was asking politely "if this seat was taken" when two burly waiters appeared from nowhere and frogmarched him towards the door, with his rolled umbrella trailing behind him.

His chums gaped in disbelief, so did we. Suddenly plates of *smørbrød* were flying. A fishball landed with a plop on an old lady's lap a few tables away. She winced and tipped it on the floor. The blue-eyed umbrella-carrying man had started grappling with the waiters. In the confusion, a jovial besweatered lumberjack put his foot on the fishball, shouted a six-letter word and skidded full tilt across the cafe floor into the four-piece band, upsetting their tiny stage. A moment later the players, still wielding their instruments, slid with great dignity into the ornamental pond beside their dais.

"What a shambles!" said Alicia with a pained expression. "I think it's time for us to leave – especially as the band has stopped playing. In any case I don't really care for water music."

We slipped out through a side door just as a carload of police shot through the main entrance.

"I don't think we should go to that place again," I said. "They're a rough lot."

To while away the next half-hour until our bus was due we went to the waiting room at the main railway station, which was situated at the opposite end of Karl Johansgate from the royal palace.

The room was dingy and sparsely furnished but we often ended up there when the weather was too cold for us to be out of doors and our pockets were too empty for us to frequent the cafes. Sometimes, when we could afford them, we sucked oranges there as it was the only place where we did not feel embarrassed at consuming such a messy snack.

One of the reasons we liked the waiting room was its entertainment value at no cost to ourselves. Smoking was banned in Norway in many public places, including the station waiting room, and we had even seen a notice on a coach telling passengers: "If you want to smoke during the trip please ask the driver to stop."

We wondered if this was to give the desperate smoker time for a quick drag, or the driver a chance to push the offender over a cliff.

In the station waiting room there was always the chance that someone would be caught having a crafty puff, and on this occasion the first sight that met our eyes was a scrawny little man being hustled out by two policemen.

"Funny!" said Alicia. "It's a busy night for the busies tonight. I expect the poor fellow was caught smoking or having a nap."

Settling down for forty winks on the hard benches was also risky as a bouncer would appear from nowhere and shake the sleeper viciously to find out if he was drunk.

"One day," said Alicia, "we'll see if we can fool them by snoring loudly in here."

On our next day off a neighbour of the Olsens offered us a lift to Oslo by car, so we did not have to wait for the bus. We learned later that there had been a landslide between there and our village minutes after our car passed by. Part of the railway and the road just beneath it had collapsed because the embankment had been undermined by seawater.

Fru Olsen, who enjoyed imparting gloomy news, told us brightly that a full bus and four cars were on the road at the time, and a house near by was crushed.

"Several people on the bus were killed and a lot hurt," she reported. Hearing the full story, we felt we had a narrow escape.

On the days we did not have the energy to go to Oslo we spent hours down by the fjordside sunbathing or swimming in the clear water. The land, which we christened Pine Paradise, was part of Herr Olsen's vast estate, and because it was a long way from the city and could be reached only through the forest, the townsfolk hadn't discovered it. We had to walk down steep paths through the pinewoods, refreshing ourselves on the way by picking the luscious wild raspberries that were as big as loganberries.

One day I nearly trod on a small brown snake that lay camouflaged among the pine needles on the path. When Alicia narrowly avoided a similar snake, reared in striking position, the following day we were quite alarmed as we were wearing open sandals.

Herr Olsen told us there were two common species of poisonous snake in Norway, so from then on we took extra care when going through the forests, especially as the paths were dotted with ants' nests. We had already discovered that an incautious step could result in nasty stings, and we used to race on tiptoe past the danger areas.

Down at the water's edge there were other nasties to be negotiated before we could have our swim. Lurking among the smooth rocks and silver sand and shingle were a host of creepy-crawlies and colourful monsters of the shallows, including prickly starfish, and we had to pick our way carefully between them to reach the deeper water.

One day we noticed some large animal footprints on the shore and learned later that a family of moose living near by had been seen by a farmer only hours beforehand.

We faced other hazards during our rambles in the forests to search for cranberries and bilberries for jam making – a job we hated but one which figured high on Fru Olsen's list of domestic priorities. On one occasion we were out walking with the four dogs when they suddenly started chasing what sounded like a herd of large animals. We couldn't see them but could hear them charging about in panic, with their bells ringing, in the undergrowth a few yards away.

Alicia screamed: "It's those bulls Fru Olsen said are left to graze in the forest. Quick, get out of the way."

Nearly all the trees were pines with only a few prickles serving for lower branches. Crouching under the undergrowth, we were pondering how to overcome the problem when three black horses stampeded past us, missing us by inches.

We didn't escape entirely unscathed as Alicia had squatted in an ants' nest and had to nurse a stinging bottom – and worse – for several days.

"Now we know the origin of the saying 'ants in your pants'," I said sympathetically.

Our early and late-season swimming activities never ceased to astonish the family, our biggest bombshell being our announcement that we had swum in the fjord in October. We had not set out with the intention of bathing, but it was such a wonderful day that we couldn't resist the temptation of a dip in the icy water.

After a quick look around to see if there were any Peeping Toms, Alicia stripped off, I kept on my bra and pants and we gingerly entered the water. A few hearty splashes and we were out again, feeling invigorated and virtuous.

We took off the worst of the wet with our underclothes and sprinted home past the snakes, ants and bulls to boast about our feat.

Mostly Alicia and I chose our own private bathing cove on Herr Olsen's land, but when we felt in need of companionship we sometimes ventured into a designated pleasure park which had been created halfway between our village and Oslo. It had little sandy beaches and a few facilities designed to attract those hardy souls who felt it worth their while to abandon the sultry pleasures of the city in favour of a dip in the sea.

The place was hard to find, for it was poorly signposted and all but the initiated would most likely drive past the narrow turning which led to the water's edge. There we used to preen ourselves in our fashionably brief bikinis, conscious that these diverted admiring male looks from the traditional one-piece costumes of the more soberly clad Norwegian women.

We noticed that the bathing area was regularly patronised by a military-looking man of wiry build, who used to fling himself with a zestful bellyflop into the icy water and strike out for one of the floating rafts to sunbathe.

"He looks as though he'd be a bit of a lad," said Alicia thoughtfully. "I wonder if he's as tough as he likes to make out."

She decided there was only one way to find out. Gracefully launching herself into the sea, she swam out to the raft and started to clamber aboard. The wiry one opened an eye, then reached down and helped her up with a strong, sinewy arm.

From the shore, where I had been joined by a young Dane as soon as my friend deserted me, I watched in amusement as Alicia proceeded to find out exactly how much of a lad her fellow sunbather was. The early stages of their acquaintance were developed on the raft, but soon they slid off it and swam to a deserted boathouse not far away.

"Aha," I thought. "The army is no match for our Alicia when she sets her traps."

Things were not quite what they seemed, however, for a few moments later the pair of them emerged from the boathouse. The military man was standing in the water and Alicia was wobbling about in a one-man canoe, trying to steer it with a paddle. I could hardly believe my eyes: she was the last person in the world I connected with this menacing sort of watersport, in which all but the most proficient were likely to end up under the water rather than on the surface.

Sure enough, in she went with an almighty splash. She was dragged up by her comrade, bundled back into the canoe and given a powerful shove. Wobble, wobble, and over she went once more. This time she disobeyed her superior officer's command, issued in his best parade-ground voice, to get back in the canoe. Woebegone and bedraggled, with a starfish stuck in her hair, she scampered out of the sea, leaving the master struggling to get the canoe back in the boathouse against a strong current.

Recovering her dignity and her breath on the shore, Alicia told me her playmate was a Polish ex-commando major named Zbigniew – she had to spell the name three times before she got it right and I understood it – who had settled in Norway after the war.

"He's rather too emaciated for my liking, but he's a sexy specimen all the same, if you can stand his bossy ways. The most offputting thing, though, is that he has a long hair on the tip of his nose which starts to quiver when he gets excited. It's a sort of warning signal to the faint-hearted, I suppose. It probably scares off the enemy

– and it scared me off, too, I can tell you. I don't like being tickled up the nose when I'm in a clinch."

"He sounds a bit of a twit to me," I said disparagingly. "I'm glad I didn't dip my toes into that Polish pool."

I gathered Alicia had experienced all she desired of Polish military tactics, for she did not refer to Zbigniew again, nor did she seem anxious to return to the bathing resort.

My poor friend had worse humiliation in store for her than a canoeing defeat, as we were soon to find out. We discovered that there was more to the moose we had recently heard about than mere footprints on the seashore. For Alicia, this extraordinary looking animal actually materialised, thanks to a chance remark of hers in an Oslo cafe one day.

The two of us were relaxing with an orange drink and talking about the footprints we had seen. So absorbed were we that for once we did not notice the Gregory Peck lookalike who was sitting at a nearby table with his ears flapping as he eavesdropped on our conversation.

"Excuse me butting in, ladies," he said suddenly. "I couldn't help overhearing what you were saying about the moose. May I join you at your table?"

"Certainly," we said in unison, making a place for him to sit between us.

It was obvious from the start that I didn't have a chance here. This gorgeous man – was it possible he really was a film star? – was paying court to my friend with all the dedication of his race. She was enchanted. I was rebuffed. But I consoled myself with our motto "Win some, lose some," and left the field to Alicia.

Our new pal, Hilmar, was inviting her to go to his fjordside farm that evening and see his pet moose.

"Pet moose?" we echoed, stupefied.

"You'll see," he promised. "I'll come and fetch you from outside the City Hall at seven o'clock and we can take it from there. Bring a needle and thimble with you, by the way."

Alicia looked taken aback. What was this? Was he expecting her to darn his socks? Time would tell, so she said nothing. It was our weekend off, so I didn't expect to see her until next day, if then.

While she was moosing, I mooched about on my own in Oslo and cheered up when a voice hailed me merrily. It was Rolf, our old sparring partner from the broadcasting centre.

"Where have you been all this time? Why didn't you come back for another tour of the studios, then?" he asked, giving me a hearty hug.

To recover lost ground we took a train into the forests of Nordmarka above the city and renewed our acquaintance in a mossy bower overlooking the glittering sea. Later we enjoyed a candlelit dinner at the Holmenkollen restaurant and rounded off a perfect evening with dancing.

It was a sad and sorry Alicia who returned home next day.

"What in heaven's name has happened to you?" I asked, seeing her raw red fingers. "Have you been picking oakum? Was he a sailor, then? I thought you would have had enough of the nautical fraternity after the third mate – or were you after another trophy like that ostentatious watch of yours?"

Alicia was very grumpy indeed. "You can think yourself lucky, my girl, that it was me he chose, otherwise you'd have been the one toiling half the night instead of gadding about in the forests with Rolf."

"Toiling half the night?" I said aghast. "What on earth do you mean? Does he run some sort of slave harem?"

"You could describe it as that, except that I was the only slave."

The story finally came out. Her film starry hero had whisked her off to his farm and put her to work embroidering a heavy blanket for Mikki, his pet moose.

I was speechless. When I regained my wits I asked: "What did you have to embroider?"

"He left it to me, so I did little daisies. He seemed to be quite happy with it," she added doubtfully.

"What about Mikki? Was he happy with it?" I said.

"I couldn't say – he spent most of the night snoring. And when a moose snores you have to hear it to believe it."

She lifted her heel. "And I bet you've never seen a moose-pat. This was quite a small animal, luckily – more of a mini-moose than a Mikki. Even so, I certainly don't want a moose loose in my hoose."

9
Happy Hitching

When we had been housemaiding for three months Herr Olsen said we had to register as foreigners working in Norway. He took us to see the local policeman, who filled in our personal details. He was particularly interested in the colour of my eyes, and as he wrote down "Brown" in his best handwriting he flashed me such a cheeky look that I went quite weak at the knees.

Now that we were really ensconced in our Norwegian niche I felt it was time we celebrated with a little holiday, so I suggested to Alicia that we should ask for a week off to do a speedy hitch-hiking tour of the fjord country.

"It will fill in the gaps in our education," she mused. "What a brilliant idea!"

Herr Olsen readily agreed to give us time off and even provided us with pocket money. He assured us it would be perfectly safe to hitch-hike in Norway as we were not likely to be molested by unwholesome characters.

His prediction turned out to be accurate. Safe it certainly was – if only because it was very nearly impossible.

"How can we get lifts when there are no cars?" Alicia whinged as, weighed down by heavy rucksacks, we trudged for mile after mile along isolated mountain roads. We crossed numerous stretches of water by ferry, took one or two local buses for short distances, and prayed for a car to come along.

"Quick, there's one now," Alicia said suddenly. "A smart white one, too. And it's slowing down."

Showing a sexy knee, she made it clear we needed a lift. We thought we were in luck as the vehicle was going very slowly, but it didn't stop and as it crawled past we saw it was a hearse with a white coffin inside.

"Don't try that on again," I said in cowed tones. "I nearly died of fright at the thought of riding in a hearse, even if it was white."

Eventually a car did come along, with two natty male Norwegians inside. By now it was getting dark and we were anxious to reach our destination – a youth hostel at the far end of one of the longest fjords – so we sat primly in the back of the car and made no attempt to display our charms.

When we arrived the warden informed us we were the first-ever people to patronise the hostel as it was newly built and had not yet even been completed. He waved airily towards the workmen who were just preparing to go home after their day's work.

Alicia's eyes lit up, but I had other things on my mind than larking about with labourers. I had already established a rapport with Torvald, the warden, a scraggy widower with a young son.

"I'm just off to inspect my field of cabbages up in the mountains," he said. "Would you like to come?"

My lifelong interest in cabbages surfaced, and I leapt nimbly into his lorry, leaving Alicia to her own devices.

The visit to the cabbage patch was instructive and I learnt a lot about Norwegian methods of cultivation – as applied to friendship. An added bonus was Torvald's offer to drive us in the morning to our next stopping place, a tourist hotel high in the Jotunheimen mountains, as he had to collect some timber from a depot near by.

When we got there we helped him load the timber on

to his lorry. We also assisted an old man who was struggling to lift some huge tree trunks on to a cart, which was hitched to a small yellow horse with a black stripe down its back – one of the sturdy fjording ponies people had described to us. They came originally from the Russian steppes 4,000 years ago but were now rapidly decreasing in numbers, so we were delighted to have spotted one.

The surrounding mountains were wild and spooky, and I could well imagine that they really were the home of the Norse giants, the Jotun, who dwelt alongside the sprites of the rivers and waterfalls. These mythical creatures and the grotesque trolls, whose carved images took pride of place among the more comely offerings in the souvenir shops, lived on in Norwegian music and culture and until the recent past many people really believed in their existence.

Torvald told us that there were more than 50 peaks in the Jotunheimen of 6,000ft or more, including the aptly named Glittertind, the "Glittering Peak", its snow-capped summit soaring to just over 8,000ft – only 60ft lower than Norway's loftiest mountain, the Galdhøpiggen.

"And there you will see the knife-edged Gjendin Ridge, where Peer Gynt rode on the back of a buck reindeer," said Torvald, pointing towards the savage backdrop of the mountain range.

We screwed up our eyes and peered into the distance, scanning the fairy pinnacles and half hoping we would see Ibsen's legendary hero on his wild ride, scattering flocks of seagulls as he hurtled through the swirling mists.

"By the way," Torvald went on, "did you know that it was your countrymen who first discovered the attractions of Norway last century and scaled many of our highest peaks?"

No, we didn't know, we said, and we were grateful for the information. We felt it entitled us to claim a tiny foothold in this country we had grown to love.

Before he left, Torvald said: "If you return this way, phone me and I'll come and fetch you." He added quietly to me, his voice tingling with suppressed excitement: "We can talk some more about cabbages and things."

Alicia's sharp ears did not miss his aside, and she gave me a withering look.

For the next stage of our journey we hitched a lift with two young Danes. They were quaking with fear on the mountain roads, which they found terrifying after their own country's flat landscape, and we felt some sympathy with them. But we were forced to admire the extraordinary feats of engineering which had provided the Norwegians with such an efficient road and rail network across and through their unyielding terrain – long tunnels blasted into the rock, roads snaking down the sheerest mountain sides, bridges spanning dizzy chasms and foaming waterfalls, supplemented by regular and reliable ferry services.

We soon found that the latter were an indispensable part of the communications network for travellers as some fjords penetrated 30 miles into the heart of the country, cutting short progress by road unless one was prepared to make an impossibly long detour. In the near vertical cliffs which tossed their shimmering waterfalls into the deep tideless waters like strands of silver hair, little wooden homes were wedged, while others clung like limpets to the rocky shoreline.

I felt almost suffocated in these steep-sided fjords and inland valleys. They bore down on me menacingly, squeezing me between their massive jaws. Alicia merely felt slightly claustrophobic. As for the two Danes with their furrowed brows and palpitating hearts, their driving was so erratic on these fearsome roads that we breathed sighs of relief when we alighted in an isolated valley, not far from a village.

Here we passed ancient wooden houses and farm buildings that could have come straight out of Oslo's folk museum. Many had turf growing on the roof – "and look, that must be a *stabbur*", I said to Alicia. "You know, one of those storehouses on log pillars where they keep their food and clothing. See, there's the steep ladder they have to climb up to get in."

The sturdy houses, mostly built of logs, were functional yet picturesque because of the carving on the gables and window surrounds. Each farm comprised quite a large number of separate buildings serving a special purpose, so that individual homesteads were more like a mini-hamlet.

An old woman in the traditional costume of the region was carrying a heavy pail of milk towards one of the sheds. She smiled at us as we passed and greeted us in a dialect that we just about understood.

"God dag," we said in reply. That was enough of an opening for her. She put down her pail and came over to us. With our Oslo Norwegian, plus a few "ums" and "ahs", questioning looks and frantic gesticulations, we managed to keep a conversation twirling as adroitly as jugglers with spinning plates, and after a while the old lady invited us to go in and join her in a glass of some indeterminate home-brew. We never discovered exactly what it was, but it made us feel very woozy.

The interior of her home was dark because the windows were so small, but the gloom was relieved by the brightly painted walls and glowing copper pans on the shelves. There were also a number of hand-painted wooden bowls and domestic utensils, as well as decorative door panels which, to us, looked centuries old. The woman herself was equally decorative in her colourful costume, and her ornate silver pendants and brooches glinted in the soft light that filtered in through the window.

Looking at her weather-beaten, kindly face, I suddenly recalled something that was written by a French travel writer in the 18th Century about the country folk of eastern Norway. They were, he wrote, "as friendly and generous as the people of Bergen were quarrelsome and greedy". I thought this description could equally well apply to the villagers of this mountainous western region. As for the people of Bergen, they sounded a rough lot, if this writer's opinion was anything to go by. I had not yet been to that city – and, I thought to myself, I don't know that I want to go, if that's what they are like.

Because we escaped from the Danish car sooner than we need have done we were faced with a three-mile walk to our next youth hostel. As we were tramping along the dusty road we could see in the distance a colourful crowd of revellers, whose laughter and voices could be heard far and wide.

"Let's go and see what they're up to," Alicia suggested. "We might be able to join in the fun, or at least get something to eat – I'm starving."

When we got nearer we saw men, women and children seated at long wooden tables in the open, being served food from large decorated bowls and drink from pewter pitchers. The merrymakers were wearing Norwegian *bunad*, national costume, but as they were dressed in widely varying styles and colours we realised they had come together from different valleys to join in the festivities.

"I wonder what they're celebrating," I said.

Then I caught sight of the pair at the head of one of the tables, and I knew what was going on – it was a traditional country wedding. The bride, in a richly embellished gown, had a golden crown on her blonde hair. Beside her sat the groom in black velvet trousers, shining white shirt frilled at the neck and cuffs, and ornately trimmed waistcoat. His round flat-topped black hat lay on the bench beside him.

Not far away was the 12th Century stave church where the wedding service had taken place. The steep, many-tiered roof with its elaborately carved gables and low porch were covered in ancient wooden shingles, and the equally ornate but windowless interior was dark and gloomy.

"It looks like something straight out of a Walt Disney fantasy," Alicia said. "You see how low the doorway is? Someone told me the reason was that enemy raiders would have to bend down to enter a stave church and the defenders inside could chop off their heads one at a time. I wonder if that's true?"

By the time we had looked round this extraordinary building the wedding party had abandoned their carousing and left the tables. They were now flinging themselves with abandon into folk dancing, weaving intricate patterns to haunting tunes played by a group of men on the *hardingfele*, the eight-stringed Hardanger fiddle, Norway's national instrument.

Star of the ensemble was an old man of nearly 80, whose nimble fingers belied his age as they darted over his gaily decorated fiddle. It was left to the younger men to perform the strenuous leaps of the *halling*, a whirling, wheeling dance originating in Hallingdal. Alicia and I watched as they tossed their hats in the air and kicked their legs as high as can-can girls.

Sure enough, it was not long before a couple of the superbly clad men noticed the two scruffy girls hovering near by in envious admiration. We were speedily unhitched from our rucksacks and drawn into the giddy fray, our walking boots and crumpled clothing standing out in sharp contrast to the gorgeous wedding apparel of the guests.

Our partners' enthusiasm was in no way diminished by the unsuitability of our gear, nor by our clumsy attempts to join in the dancing. The other participants welcomed our intrusion graciously, and in no time at all we felt less ill at ease, though our attempts at conversation were hampered by our inability to understand their dialect.

"But who needs conversation?" Alicia murmured when the dancing ended, as her beau led her off to a barn to share an impromptu picnic salvaged from the remains of the wedding feast.

I was inclined to agree as I accompanied Bjørn, my partner, to a sheltered spot beside the fjord to relax after our exertions – "though I wouldn't describe the dance he led me as relaxing", I told Alicia later. "His high kicks were even more energetic than they were in the *halling* and that was only the start of his antics."

I recounted how Bjørn – "his name means 'bear' " – had made a fool of himself by prancing across a dozen or so loose logs that were floating near the edge of the water, boasting that he could emulate the feat of King Olav I, who used to run across the outstretched oars of a Viking ship above the waves.

"But in Bjørn's case pride came before a fall, for he was only halfway across when he fell into the fjord in all his finery and vanished under the logs," I said. "When he surfaced his velvet suit had shrunk so much that he had to strip off, and his hat was last seen floating away in the distance.

"Next thing we knew his angry old mother came steaming up the path, ranting and raving because he had ruined his brother's outfit. She chased him back home, bare bum and all, wielding a pitchfork – and that was the last I saw of him."

"Trust you to end up with a bare bear!" said Alicia.

When it began to get dark we set off to find the youth hostel, which was not far away. It turned out to be an ancient log hut with turf and little trees covering the roof and an old lady as warden. It was here that I had my greatest linguistic triumph. After I had asked for beds for the night and explained that we did not have time to book in advance, the old lady handed me a registration form – the simple type Norwegians had to fill in, not the full "questionnaire" presented to foreigners.

I was so flattered at being mistaken for one of her countrywomen that I did not even flinch when she set before us two steaming bowls of *fiskesuppe*. The fishy smell had already warned us of impending horror but we smiled gratefully and said: "How delicious!"

Alicia shut her eyes, as though in eager anticipation, and started sipping the soup. I was about to follow suit when the old lady went into the kitchen to see to the next course. Quick as a flash I tiptoed to the corner and emptied the soup into the dog's bowl.

Seeing my dish empty, the old lady was plainly delighted that I had enjoyed her soup so much.

Encouraged vengefully by Alicia, who had forced herself to eat most of hers, she prepared to give me a second helping. Only the antics of the dog, which was wagging its tail expectantly at the prospect of seconds, diverted our hostess from the bowl of fish soup.

"Ragnar has certainly taken a liking to you, my dear," she said as I hastily gathered up my dish and took it to the kitchen, followed by the drooling hound.

"I'm glad someone likes that disgusting stuff," Alicia whispered. "I don't know how I've managed to keep it down."

She was not so lucky at our next youth hostel, where meatballs were on the menu. She must have been served a duff portion because she was very sick in the night, to the consternation of two Swedish women sharing our quarters.

After three visits to the bathroom a white-faced Alicia eventually crawled into bed and fell asleep. She had a bad night, though, twitching restlessly and muttering in her sleep in Norwegian, which prompted one or other of the Swedish women to jump out of bed and feel her forehead or pulse.

"Frustrated nurses, perhaps," I thought, only too glad I could leave it to someone else to tend to my ailing friend. I had never fancied myself as a Florence Nightingale.

By morning Alicia had recovered her colour and composure sufficiently for us to continue on our way, though she still felt very fragile. Armed with our youth hostel maps, we arrived at our next destination, a remote mountain hamlet, late in the evening after a tiring trek through deep snow which left Alicia feeling more fragile than ever. We had got lost and found ourselves crossing an isolated mountain pass, stumbling over slippery rocks and unwillingly paddling in fast-flowing streams. Our boots and trousers were sodden, our noses glowing bright red and our tempers frayed.

"Right, so where's this wretched hostel?" Alicia croaked. "It must be one of these five houses."

How wrong we were! A young man informed us that none of the five houses was a youth hostel – "and there has never been one anywhere near here," he added firmly.

Alicia waved the map accusingly under his nose. "Well, it's clearly marked on this."

I snarled: "A fine mess we've got ourselves into. What are we going to do? It's too late to go on, and anyway there's no bus."

We were resigning ourselves to creeping under a damp hayrick – "and I hope it's not full of earwigs," I said crossly – when the young man said: "You don't have to do that, my love. There's plenty of room in our house. Only my brother and I are at home. Our parents are away."

By now his twin brother had joined us and the two introduced themselves as Odd and Ole Bodd. There was an ominous silence as we digested this information. Was it a joke? I wondered. Surely even Norwegians couldn't have such unlikely names?

Alicia spluttered as she tried to stifle her mirth. Odd Bodd shot her a poisonous look and she hastily disguised her *faux pas* with an exaggerated sneeze which prompted Ole (pronounced "Ooler") to say: "You get out of those wet trousers and have a nice hot bath."

We smiled bashfully and thanked him as we went indoors, much mollified at the prospect of a hot bath.

"Where's the bathroom?" Alicia asked, eager to restore herself to her usual pristine loveliness.

With a flourish, Ole unhooked a huge tin bathtub from a nail on the wall and plonked it down in front of the blazing log fire while his brother hung a cauldron of water to heat above the flames.

"There you are, ladies," said Odd.

The glow from the oil lamp caught an unmistakable gleam of anticipation in his blue eyes as he sloshed hot water into the tub and beckoned us to get in.

"You have a nice soak and afterwards we'll give you a good rub down. If you are still cold after that we'll warm ourselves up under the duvets."

I slept fitfully that night as a nonsense rhyme kept buzzing about in my head like a mad bee. It was still there next morning and I recited it to Alicia:

Though one might think to have a name
Like Ole Bodd is very odd,
His twin has greater claim to fame
For Odd's an even odder Bodd.

We were still laughing about our preposterous escapade with the Odd twins as we stepped out refreshed into the cold mountain air to continue our journey.

Our next stop was at another hideaway hamlet, with only a tiny white church and two houses to justify its inclusion on our map.

"Well, this time there's no mistake," I said. "This must be the hostel because the other house is the parson's – I can see him on his knees in the kitchen, praying."

"Probably asking God to make sure that what he's about to receive isn't fishballs," said Alicia dryly.

The other house was in darkness and there was no answer when we tinkled the cowbell hanging by the door, so we went in. It was still light and on the table an appetising-looking cold meal was laid out.

"There must have been some telepathy at work as we didn't book in advance," I said. "There's only one plate but there's plenty here for two."

We sat down and greedily demolished the cold pheasant, washing it down with the red wine which was standing by. We toasted our absent host or hostess and Alicia said languidly: "In Norway I suppose it's quite safe to leave your house unlocked. You couldn't do that in England – anyone could walk in and gobble up the food."

The wine and warmth from the corner stove had made us drowsy. We were too sleepy to search for the bathroom, which seemed to be missing, so we crawled into the only bed we could find.

Alicia yawned. "The warden probably sleeps somewhere else. I had an aunt who used to sleep in the garage on a deckchair so she could let out her bedroom to tourists."

We had to lie in the bed top-to-toe. Alicia suddenly

sat up, holding her nose and frowning. "For heaven's sake wrap your feet up in something – they're humming."

Her own feet, though they had been toiling up hill and down dale as arduously as mine, were still daisy fresh, and I contented myself with tickling them maliciously with a feather before we both slipped gently into dreamland.

I was jerked back to consciousness by someone shaking me roughly. Still half asleep, I focussed a bleary eye on a bushy, frost-covered beard which sprouted from a ginger-haired giant with a shotgun and a lot of furry corpses slung round his powerful neck.

I cringed beneath the duvet as he roared: "What are you doing in my bed?"

"Your bed?" I stammered, cowering.

"Certainly. And you've eaten all my food."

By this time Alicia, looking disarmingly bewildered, was sitting up, her tousled hair falling softly on her white shoulders. The giant's ferocious eyes swivelled in her direction.

"Aha, so there are two of you," he bellowed. His voice softened as he added indulgently: "I don't remember catching such dainty quarry when I was out hunting."

Explanations were obviously going to take some time and the frosted giant was cold. We made room for him and he squeezed into bed with us, pushing us into a corner. His thick woollen socks steamed but Alicia didn't dare complain . . .

Owing to the lack of traffic we had to continue our journey next day by bus, which was a nerve-racking experience. On the devilish Trollstigveien the driver had to perform a series of precarious manoeuvres to negotiate the numerous hair-raising bends, reversing six times at one point. We were sitting in the rear, which jutted out beyond the wheels, and shuddered as we found ourselves above a sheer drop on each occasion.

There was still so much snow lying on the slopes in this region that people were skiing, lazily watched by scantily clad sunbathers on the glistening rocks. As the bus passed we caught sight of three strapping males, stark naked, who emerged from a tourist hut and rolled in the snow with shouts of laughter.

In several places the road was blocked by minor snowfalls, and some of the male passengers grabbed shovels from the luggage compartment and helped the driver clear the way.

Time was marching on and we were due back at our domestic posts in the next few days, so we had decided not to dawdle but to return home by the shortest route. We telephoned Torvald, our friendly youth hostel warden with the lorry, and he promised to meet us at a small village further down the valley.

He arrived minus lorry, to our disappointment, as we were relying on a lift to Oslo.

"You didn't work the oracle this time," Alicia sneered while Torvald was out of earshot. "You must be losing your touch. There won't be any visits to cabbage patches this time – serves you right. What's more, we'll have to go by train to Oslo after all unless you can wheedle a lift from someone else."

Torvald decided to spend the night in the same hotel as us. We all went to the cinema to see a smutty Swedish film and then stayed up dancing. After our educational experiences at the wedding reception, we were able to show off in the folk dances and felt justifiably complacent when we matched our dignified movements against the undisciplined cavorting of the other hotel guests.

Next day, after this rollicking evening, we were tired out. However, we decided to save money by trying to hitch a lift to the next youth hostel instead of taking the train to Oslo, as we still had a few days in hand.

We failed to get any lifts – and then we failed to locate the youth hostel, so we decided to spoil ourselves after our gruelling walk and spend the night in a modest pension run by Einar, a large, ex-champion boxer with a gammy leg, and his even larger wife. The couple immediately made us feel at home and we were invited to wash away the day's grime before *aftens*.

We had been hankering for a hot bath, and here at last was a chance to cosset ourselves after our harum-scarum carryings-on. We were relieved to find that our ablutions – "we don't have a bath, but you can have a shower," said our host – would be performed under more civilised conditions than those offered by Odd and Ole Bodd, though we were slightly taken aback to discover that the shower "cubicle" was a vast room in the attic with a drain in the middle of the lino floor.

There was plenty of room for us to shower together – plus a trio of 5ft Japanese men who burst in unannounced to join in the watery merrymaking. Then, pink and shining with cleanliness and exertion, we went downstairs and seated ourselves in the tiny dining-room.

The evening's jollity was not yet over. No sooner was the meal ended than a handful of rowdy "regulars" who frequented the tiny bar sneaked into the adjoining residents' lounge to cast befuddled but lustful looks at the two foreign females who had come into their midst.

Meanwhile, shouts of "*Skål!*" could be heard in the bar, where the local postman was entertaining his chums on a prodigious accordion of a type I had never seen before. He was accompanying what sounded like at least half a dozen hearty men roaring out bawdy Norwegian and British songs. A peek round the corner revealed, however, that there were only two singers – one of the barmen and the ebullient Einar, whose vocal powers obviously equalled or even surpassed his reputed prowess in the boxing ring. He was thumping with his good leg in time to the music while his listeners clapped vigorously.

While Einar's attention was diverted an inebriated man sidled up to me, caressing my cheek and burbling in a maudlin voice about my "fiery brown eyes" and my beguiling beauty. He regaled me with an account of his wife's two operations, assuring me that she was "better now". I was startled to learn, as he grew drunker, that in fact she had died two years earlier.

"But you said she was better," I expostulated.

"Yes," was the slurred reply. "She's better now. She is dead."

Einar had taken a respite from his vocal exertions and had come into the lounge, where he gave my quirky admirer a stern ticking off.

"If I played you a record in the morning of all your gibberish you wouldn't believe it," he said.

I asked Einar next day whether the man's wife was alive or dead – "or does he just have a warped sense of humour?"

"She is very much alive," he said. "She is matron at the local hospital. And she has never had an operation in her life."

Alicia, it turned out, had been entertained by an even more outlandish character, who told her he had radio waves in his head and claimed he was Jesus – and Hitler was God.

Mentally exhausted after our encounter with these weirdos, we fell into bed well after midnight hoping for a good night's sleep before the next day's exertions. The sing-song in the bar had started up again and Einar's bellowing voice mingled with the raucous laughter of his boozy patrons as the Saturday night binge staggered on into the early hours of Sunday morning. As our bedroom was on the ground floor, and on the same side of the hotel as the bar, there was no way we could shut out the din.

"Fat hope we've got of getting any sleep tonight," said Alicia. "We might just as well have stayed up and joined in the debauchery."

"I don't think I could stand any more of the sort of socialising I've experienced this evening," I replied. "And our innocent little minds would be sullied beyond redemption if we had much more of that sort of junket."

We could hear little knots of young people talking in loud voices in the courtyard outside our window, and every now and then there were cackles of laughter from the girls, who were just as sozzled as the men.

"The Japs are out there," said Alicia, peeking out from behind the curtains of our bedroom window. "And some of the others are staying in this hotel, too. If they're not careful they'll find themselves locked out, because the doors close any minute now and there's no night porter."

I wasn't in the least sympathetic. "That's their problem. The night's quite warm, so they can sleep under a hedge. Anyway, it will soon be morning."

Fifteen minutes later I found it wasn't their problem after all – it was ours. Things were a bit quieter outside now, and we were just beginning to doze off when we heard an insistent tapping at our window. We ignored it, but it persisted, so in the end I got out of bed and opened the window.

A drunken girl gave what she fondly hoped was a penitent smile. "We're locked out of the hotel, I'm afraid. Can we please come in through your window?"

I wasn't pleased. "Is it just you?"

She hesitated. "No, my friends are with me."

"Well, how many of you are there, then?"

Again the hesitation. "Well, er, only . . . five."

"Humph," I said gruffly. "I suppose you'd better come in, then. But be quick about it – we're trying to get to sleep."

I stood back and waited while three men and two girls hoisted themselves drunkenly through the window and stamped across my bed, which was just beneath it, leaving dirty footprints on my duvet cover.

"Thank you very much, my darling," said one of the men, lurching towards me and pecking me on the cheek. He was preparing to favour me with more affectionate expressions of his gratitude when one of the girls grabbed him by the hair and yanked him unceremoniously towards the door. His parting words, "See you later, sweetheart," faded away down the corridor.

Alicia was sitting up in bed looking bewildered.

"What's going on?" she said. "I was half asleep and suddenly there were people crashing about all over the room."

"Go back to sleep – they've all gone now," I told her.

I was wrong again. More tapping at the window, more men and girls jumping down on to my bed. The influx of locked-out guests continued, with the three Japanese men at the tail end of the procession. They drifted across the carpet as silently as phantoms, hissing: "Thank you velly, velly much."

"They were all sloshed," I said furiously as Alicia and I settled down at four o'clock in the morning to try to get a few hours' sleep. "We'd better make sure we never get a ground-floor bedroom again."

When we told Einar about our nocturnal invasion next morning he was profoundly apologetic.

"I know this goes on sometimes, but as we sleep on the far side of the hotel we don't hear anything," he explained. "I'll have to put up a large sign warning guests that they are not to disturb people in the ground-floor bedroom."

We said nothing. We knew quite well that it would take more than a large sign to keep out partying Norwegians bent on creeping back to the fold.

As we were leaving the pension, Einar's wife hurried in to reception in a panic. She had just realised she had double-booked a football team and a Salvation Army band for the following week and was wondering which group to accommodate in the cellar.

"Probably tossing up whether the church folk will be more likely to accept the discomfort with a good grace or whether the footballers won't notice the hard floor," said Alicia as we marched off, grateful that we had not been relegated to the nether regions.

"That's probably where the Japs have been – they disappeared after dinner," I commented. "I would have thought they could have found their way back down there through a coal hatch or something."

Our last stop before returning to Oslo was in a largish town which boasted a splendid youth hostel complete with riverside swimming pool. To reach the hostel we had to walk through an area of woodland, where we passed a man busy trimming the branches of a tall tree. He paused long enough to give a piercing wolf whistle, nearly falling off his ladder when he craned his neck to watch us as we picked our way along the rocky path.

Alicia nudged me and pointed back to where the man was now sawing vigorously.

"See what he's doing?" she said.

I was puzzled. Then light dawned just as man, ladder and branch crashed to the ground. Like a character in an old crazy movie, he had set up his ladder on the wrong side of the cut.

Alicia sighed. "A ludicrous end to a loony holiday, but boy, was it fun!"

10
The Frozen North

Herr Olsen, a most generous employer, announced one day early in July that we needed a proper holiday. Having only just returned from our hitch-hiking exploits we were surprised, but gratified.

"So," continued the master of the house, "I have booked a two-week trip for you to the North Cape so you can see the midnight sun."

We gasped and were lost for words.

"You will travel up by land and down by coastal steamer," Herr Olsen went on. "It is all arranged and you leave next week."

Time crawled as we dreamed of our trip to the Land of the Midnight Sun. Fru Olsen, the eternal pessimist, told us in her melancholy voice that we would probably have bad weather and not see the sun at all, let alone at midnight.

"One man went there nine times and did not see it once," she said, adding for good measure: "And two boats have run aground and been abandoned on the way up the coast this week."

By now we knew Fru Olsen well enough not to be put off by her dismal predictions.

"I wonder what the scenery will be like," I said.

"And the men," Alicia added. "Will they be fierce Eskimos or something? Fighting with knives?"

"It's Finns who fight with knives," I said. "It's Lapps who live up there with their reindeer, and they are a peaceful race."

"The Finn I found in Oslo had no need of a knife to get his own way," Alicia smirked. "But I've heard the folk up north are all rather eccentric. They sleep all day in the winter and play all night in the summer. Could be fun."

At last the great day came when we set off for Trondheim, the country's third largest city, where the kings of Norway were crowned. We arrived late in the day so our sightseeing was confined to the magnificent Nidaros Cathedral, started in 1152 and built as a monument to the king who converted Norway to Christianity and who was later canonised as Saint Olav. The building, ravaged by fire several times, was said to be the finest example of medieval architecture in Scandinavia. It was now in its final stages of restoration, begun in 1869, and was not expected to be completed for at least 30 years.

Next day we boarded the northbound train again. Over the Tannoy came the announcement: "Next stop Hell."

"Have we been that naughty?" I said to Alicia.

Hell was a small but important railway junction, for it was there that passengers bound for Sweden had to change to complete the 534-mile journey from Trondheim to Stockholm. We did not linger in Hell but sped on to Lønsdal, high on a mountain plateau just inside the Arctic Circle, where the northern express railway ended. A modest circular marker beside the railway indicated the point where we entered the polar region of this 1,000-mile-long country.

A fellow passenger informed us that the coastline, including bays, fjords and inlets, extended to more than 13,000 miles and that it was guarded by some 150,000 islands and islets. Consulting our map, we felt it an apt description that Norway, only four miles wide in the middle, was shaped like a tadpole swimming south.

As we sped up the "tail" of the tadpole we kept our

fingers crossed that Fru Olsen's pessimistic forecast about the midnight sun would prove to be ill-founded. Our luck was in. The sun never set and we were beginning to feel quite frisky with all this warmth. In the hotel were plenty of young Norwegian men, who were also feeling frisky, and we danced well into the small hours.

It was here that we joined the party of people who were to continue the journey with us to the North Cape. It consisted of six elderly Norwegian couples, two Swedish spinsters, a middle-aged Dane, an eminently respectable Swiss man, an enthusiastic young female guide called Edvarda – and a very saucy driver.

Nobody would speak to the Swiss man because they all thought he was German and they still had vivid memories of the Occupation. I pointed out that he was wearing a little red cross badge in his lapel and spoke Swiss German, but the others still shunned him.

Apart from us and the guide, the bus driver was the only member of the party under 40. He was quick to take note of this fact, and as he slickly managed his gearbox on the terrifying hairpin bends he threw frequent sidelong glances at us where we sat demurely in the front seat, nearly beside him.

The two Swedish ladies sat behind us and chatted with us incessantly over our shoulders. They understood our much improved Norwegian and we understood most of their Swedish, so the conversation flowed fairly easily. It lapsed only when the driver stopped the bus at the most dramatic viewpoints so that everyone could get out to admire the foaming waterfalls or glittering glaciers.

There was also a brief interlude in the conversation when two elderly Norwegian men started paying the Swedish ladies surreptitious court while their wives were having a nap. Alicia and I turned our attention to the driver, studying him closely.

"See how he handles the wheel," said Alicia admiringly. "A forceful type, obviously. I wonder what he does during the overnight stops."

We soon found out. By the evening Alicia and I were tired and ready for our meal. The bus driver ate at the same table as the passengers and mingled with them – or rather, with us. He flashed his perfect teeth, smoothed back his blond hair, and asked: "Are you two enjoying the trip, then?"

"We certainly are," we cooed in unison, flashing our perfect teeth and tossing our dark tresses. Dark tresses, we had soon learned, were the way to a man's heart in the land of the blond Viking.

The driver told us we would be stopping at all the main towns of North Norway, including Bodø, Narvik, a name we were familiar with from wartime reports, Tromsø, euphemistically known as "The Paris of the North", and the Lapp town of Karasjok.

"How many days do we have north of the Arctic Circle?" Alicia asked.

"Six days this side of North Cape – and six nights," he added suggestively.

Alicia said: "I'm told people in the north never go to bed in the summer."

He smiled lecherously. "They do, but just for two or three hours. And that's long enough . . ."

I did not altogether care for his manner, so I said coldly: "We'll be far too busy to go to bed, anyway."

His leer grew more objectionable and I was suddenly reminded of the chief engineer and his snapping teeth.

"How disappointing," he breathed. "And do you, too, anticipate being too busy?" he asked Alicia.

She apparently did not have unpleasant memories of snapping teeth.

"That depends," she chirped. "I expect I shall need just a little sleep."

I sighed. It sounded as though my friend was destined to get rather deeply involved with this fellow and I was glad to be sitting this one out. As fate had it, the bus driver's bedroom that night was sandwiched between our rooms. I locked my door and listened. Stealthy footsteps, a gentle click as a door handle turned, then silence.

"You won't be surprised to learn that his name's Randi – and it suits him very well," she said next day.

"But surely Randi is a girl's name?" I said.

"Yes, it is. He told me his mother wanted a girl so badly that when he was born she refused to abandon the name she had chosen for a daughter. He doesn't seem to mind, though – and I can assure you he's no sissy!"

On the way to Bodø, our next stop, Alicia relaxed in her seat and watched Randi through half-closed lids. He gave her a sly wink from time to time and when there was an opportunity he reached out and patted her knee in a very friendly way.

At Bodø we went to see the Saltstraum, the infamous maelstrøm, where many ships had been sucked into the whirlpool over the years. From the rocks we watched the deceptively innocent-looking 16-knot bore rushing through the narrow gap between two shores, only the vortexes midstream hinting at its evil nature. Large gulls were floating serenely in the middle of the whirlpool and a small motor boat with a man and boy on board was making its way across the edge of the danger area. I expected to see it, and the gulls, vanish into the depths, but nothing so melodramatic happened.

"But the boat would be in trouble if its engine packed up," the guide explained. "It is only safe for ships to pass two hours in every 24, so I hope they know what they're doing."

The wily bus driver knew what he was doing, too, I noticed. Thanks to him I saw little of Alicia these days.

I was not left alone to mope, though, for I kept company with the older passengers, who were friendly and only too willing to instruct me in the finer points of their native tongue. I had already discovered this was in a perpetual state of flux, with New Norwegian – a compound of dialects – beginning to poke its nose cheekily into the territory of the traditional Danish-influenced "book" Norwegian.

I now learnt that an even deadlier trap lay in wait for ambitious foreigners hoping to become proficient in the language, for they would have to master two perplexing types of speech melody known as the "double tone" and "single tone", a linguistic peculiarity which imparts to Norwegian and Swedish their distinctive rising cadence.

Herr Dahl, one of the elderly Norwegians, explained patiently that some words were spelt differently but sounded the same apart from their tone. He reinforced this vital message with a comical series of sing-song sounds, but my untrained ear still failed to detect the subtle difference between the Norwegian words for "farmer" and "beans". I consoled myself with the thought that the worst that could happen, should I choose the wrong tone, would be the acquisition of a brace of earthy farmers instead of a plate of boring beans – a mistake that might well work in our favour.

I found it hard to converse with the stolid Dane as he swallowed all his words, so part of our conversation had to be in written form. This I understood easily, as Norwegian and Danish were so similar, except that Danish was not plagued by tonal acrobatics.

All the Norwegians were very churlish towards Hans, the Swiss man, even though they could have conversed in English had they wished, so it was left to me to keep him company. When his English failed him we spoke in German, but I found this very confusing as many words turned willy-nilly into similar Norwegian words halfway through the sentence, entirely without my blessing.

One day Hans and I were wandering on the cliffs during a halt for refreshments when we came to a small lighthouse. We were walking round it to look at the sea when the lighthouse keeper suddenly popped out of a doorway like a jack-in-the-box.

Hailing us blithely, he came hurrying towards us. He was a spry and sporty fellow and I quite fancied him.

"Hello, folks!" he called. "Welcome to my little lighthouse. You come round this side – it's werry windy over there."

"Yes, very vindy," echoed Hans, turning up his coat collar.

The lighthouse keeper issued an invitation to inspect his lighthouse. I accepted with alacrity and was pleased when Hans was hesitant.

"If you don't want to climb all those stairs, don't worry, I'll go on my own," I said, hoping he would skip this tiring treat. I looked expectantly at the keeper, who was a little tipsy, and was vexed to see he wasn't looking at me at all. His eyes were on my companion as he said in a surly voice: "Off you go, little girl, this is no place for you. A lighthouse is a man's domain."

I was dumbfounded. It was the first time I'd been upstaged by an elderly man. Hans was dumbfounded, too, and embarrassed. He beat a hasty retreat as the lighthouse keeper tried to take his arm and propel him into his lofty lair.

"Good heavens!" I exclaimed. "So it was you he fancied. Jammy! You were obviously going to be treated to a Swiss roll."

Hans laughed. "I saw that from the moment he appeared. I hope your vanity isn't too ruffled?"

"Not at all. I still say I'm prettier than you!"

11
Pining for their Shadows

The most thrilling part of our journey still lay before us as we forged ahead into the breathtakingly beautiful Land of the Midnight Sun, where even most Norwegians had never set foot.

The route from Bodø to Narvik, a busy port shipping iron ore from nearby Sweden, included four ferry crossings. The waters around Narvik were dotted with sunken vessels, a relic, we assumed, of the battle in May 1940 when an Allied expeditionary force captured the town from the Germans and had to withdraw two weeks later.

The most interesting shipwreck, however, was to be seen near Tromsø, the largest town in North Norway. Here Alicia and her admirer deigned to abandon their wanton wanderings and join the rest of us on a motor boat trip around the fjord to see the wreck of the German battleship *Tirpitz*, which was sunk by the RAF during the war and was now being dismantled.

The local inhabitants still had vivid memories of standing on the hillside in 1944 to watch the drama of one of the world's largest battleships turning turtle after being attacked by British bombers. An old man told me he saw survivors crawling all over the hull, many in their underclothes and covered in oil.

"We could hear others trapped inside, knocking for hours on end," he said. "But more than 1,000 men died. There were so many corpses in the water than none of us would eat fish from the fjord after that."

When we went round the quaint old town – one of the few which escaped being razed by the retreating Germans – we all posed for photographs beside the stuffed polar bear which dominated the pavement outside a photographic shop.

I had by now got used to seeing the sun shining brightly all night, and as some hotel bedroom windows had only net curtains it was obvious the northerners did not expect their guests to sleep. So I gave up any attempt at going to bed, and while Alicia and Randi disported themselves I knew not where, I went for a midnight stroll.

People were still out and about in the early hours chatting at garden gates, and some boys were enjoying a game of football at three o'clock in the morning. Farm workers toiled steadily through the night, gathering their brief but abundant harvest in preparation for the long, dark winter that would all too soon close in on them.

To my surprise I found I didn't need any sleep as long as the sun shone, though I did doze fitfully for an hour or two most nights. Alicia seemed to be living at the same intense pace as the northerners who crammed so much into so short a time before sinking back into sombre hibernation.

It was in Tromsø that I had my first real insight into the offbeat phenomenon that characterised North Norway. I had never before tried to visualise how it would feel to be blessed by a never-setting sun for weeks on end, only to be dragged into the deepest gloom by a never-rising sun in the winter.

Looking around at the faces of passers-by, I could now understand the comment by the Norwegian author Knut Hamsun in his novel *Pan*, set in North Norway, that the people were "strange and of a different nature to any he had met before". He wrote that one summer's night was enough to change a child into a mature adult.

But as winter closed in a "secretive stillness" came over the people – "they brooded silently, their eyes waited for winter".

As this was summer I was not able to witness this singular transformation, but I learnt more about it from an impetuous young farmer who accosted me while I was watching the football.

"Hi, there!" he shouted as he clambered over a fence from his field and sat beside me. He was determined to prove that he had plenty of summer vigour, and the moment the footballers dispersed he inveigled me into helping him stack the last of his hay – "and then, my love, I'll teach you about our mysterious northern yearnings".

My educational session in the hayloft was largely verbal, punctuated by short, lively exercises of a practical nature. My mentor told me his name was Peter – "it's usually shortened to Per" – and he had lived in Tromsø all his life.

"You see, we have to work all the hours there are in summer – and that's when we do our loving, too," he added with an affectionate squeeze. "In the winter darkness we get too tired. Some of us can't sleep, others of us sleep so long we don't know whether it's morning or evening when we wake. We get disoriented because our body clocks run amok."

I said: "It sounds as though Hamlet must have been to the Arctic, the way he spoke of time being out of joint. Perhaps he wasn't a Dane after all."

Peter said a few people found their creative talents were at their peak in the winter – "but for most of us time drags. We get so depressed that we either sleep or get drunk. We withdraw into our shells, our beds or the bars. You'll find all the bars crammed in the winter."

I asked him when the sun would desert them.

"On November 25. It returns on January 21, which

we call Sun Day, just for a few minutes. We keep our fingers crossed that it won't be cloudy that day and ruin the great moment we've all been watching and waiting for. It's like coming out of a claustrophobic cupboard – and best of all, it means we can see our shadows again."

The thought of people pining for their shadows intrigued me no end. Like most of my friends, I'd always taken mine for granted.

Seeing my dubious look, Peter said: "I'm serious. A lot of us are really spooked by losing our shadows."

I asked if he had ever heard of another Peter, Peter Schlemihl, hero of a 19th Century German fantasy, who bartered with the devil to exchange his shadow for a bottomless purse of money.

"The devil rolled up the shadow, folded it and put it in his pocket," I said. "Peter Schlemihl soon found out to his cost how awkward life was without his shadow. People jeered at him and generally made his life a misery. But when the devil offered to give him back his shadow in exchange for his soul, he refused. He didn't think that was a good bargain.

"All you folk up here seem to be wiser than he was – I can see you rejoice in your shadows and cling to them as long as you can."

Peter told me Sun Day was declared a school holiday in 1873 by the king because it fell on the same date as his birthday. The occasion used to be celebrated with feasting, pageantry and the election of a Sun King and Sun Princess. Much of this had changed, but even today some of the older men and women kept alive the age-old mystique of the north, telling tales of how the Huldra, the temptress with a hidden cow's tail, seduced young shepherds, who lost track of time in her arms.

When I commiserated with him on this doleful burden of darkness which weighed them all down, he said brightly: "Of course, there are compensations. We have the magical northern lights which flash across the sky in winter like a fairy firework display."

He said there were all kinds of myths and legends connected with these dazzling manifestations – sometimes known as the Merry Dancers – which were caused by solar eruptions scattering millions of tiny particles. These were caught in Earth's magnetic field and collided with atoms and molecules in the atmosphere, causing them to emit light.

When this absorbing lecture had ended Peter and I enjoyed a hearty frolic in the hay and I then returned to the fold to join the rest of our party, who were about to board the coach. From that moment on I looked with new respect at the good, solid shadows which these moody people of the north trailed behind or pushed in front of them so joyously.

Alicia's natural shadow was not much in evidence these days as she spent a lot of time out of the sun with her substitute shadow, Randi.

"You're beginning to look a bit peaky," I told her sarcastically on one of our rare encounters, this time in Alta. "Perhaps a day or two in the fresh air would do you good."

"On the contrary, I'm feeling very refreshed. I hope you are finding plenty to do with all those nice couples."

I was irritated by her tone and was glad we had only one more night to spend on land before leaving the coach – and its driver – at Hamnbukt. There we were to join a small steamer, the Sørøy, which would take us to a tiny landing stage at Hornvika, below North Cape.

Alta could claim more than a fair share of fame for its modest size. For a start the area had some of the finest prehistoric rock carvings in Europe, many of the 1,700 hunting scenes thought to be up to 6,000 years old. It had also, in the 18th Century, been the scene of a bloody feud following a pietistic revival movement instigated by a Swedish priest, Lars Levi Laestadius, among the Lapps in an attempt to curb their unbridled drinking

Law and order was eventually restored by a unit of 50 infantrymen. This drastic measure was destined to be echoed more than 100 years later, in 1981, when 600 police officers forcibly removed a chain of Lapp and conservationist protesters from the site of a 377ft dam planned to provide 30,000 homes with power – a project that became Norway's most contentious issue and reached fruition in 1987.

Alicia and I learned that the movement founded by the Swedish priest Laestadius still attracted supporters 100 years after its inception. We also discovered to our cost that Alta was still a stronghold of the Finns, who settled in the area in large numbers in the previous century after being driven from their native forests by famine. Our hotel turned out to be their favourite stamping ground, and plenty of stamping and quarrelling was going on among the crowd of hot-headed young men drinking at the bar and telling ribald jokes. They were very blond, very savage – and all carried knives.

Alicia unwisely gave the merest hint of a wiggle. Seconds later steel blades were flashing as two young Finns fought for her favour. The five-minute battle was waged to a chorus of cheers and stamping, and when it came to an abrupt end I was awarded the loser. His handsome face, already scarred from past affrays, now boasted a new gash. He seemed totally oblivious of his wound but graciously accepted my timid offer of a dainty lace hankie to press to his cheek, and while I was consoling him for his defeat the victor carried Alicia off to some dark nook in the bar like the spoils of war.

Our last stop was at Karasjok, a Lapp town in Finnmark, Norway's largest county, which covers 15 per cent of the country's area yet has only two per cent of the population. On the way there we called in at a nomad Lapp settlement where the Samer, as they were called, were living in tents and tending herds of reindeer for a livelihood.

They were a fascinating bunch in their brightly coloured caps and tunics and reindeer skin leggings. We were surprised that they were able to chat with us in Norwegian, although they used their own Samisk language among themselves.

As we were taking photographs of them, their tents, their dogs and their cooking pots hanging from wooden poles erected tripod-fashion over the open fire, I caught Alicia ogling one of the young men. Like his companions he had a flat, round face and pale Mongoloid features and looked nothing like the Nordic types we normally fancied.

He smiled at her shyly as he sat down in front of the fire near the circle of tents. Then, weary from his day's trek, he eased off his skin boots and wiggled his grimy toes. Alicia pulled a face as steam and a pungent smell issued from the hot hay stuffed inside the boots, where the young Lapp had been simmering his feet.

"That put you off, then! And it's a good job Fru Olsen isn't here – she would think that very naysty," I laughed.

We climbed back into the coach to hear from Edvarda about the tumultuous past of the Samer and their desperate attempts to cling to their cultural identity. This was continually being eroded by the Norwegians, who conquered them and still classed them as an inferior race.

The origin of this untamed nomad people was shrouded in mystery, said Edvarda. Their esoteric religious rites, rapt worship of nature and supposed magic powers had over the centuries aroused fear and suspicion among their Nordic countrymen, who not only exploited the Lapps mercilessly in the field of trade, taxation and territory but also instigated a savage reign of terror in the 18th Century in a drive to force them to embrace Christianity.

The Norwegianisation process began in earnest in the 1850s. In 1902 the Samer were deprived of the right to buy their own land if they could not speak Norwegian – a law which was to remain in force for more than 60 years. To us in the mid-20th Century, it was apparent that they were still second-class citizens, though they seemed carefree and proud. No wonder, we thought, when a Lapp with more than 500 animals was deemed rich.

Edvarda said there were some 20,000 Lapps in Norway, including 7,000 nomads, and only 10,000 in Sweden, Finland and Russia together. Some earned a living from the sea, others from their reindeer. These herdsmen and their families chewed dried, uncooked reindeer meat while on the move – we were given a piece to taste and found it as uninspiring as a hunk of old brown leather – and made "bread" of dried reindeer blood and milk.

Alicia and I would have liked to search for *multer*, the exclusive cloudberries which looked like yellow raspberries and grew only there on the vast expanses of scrub-covered tundra, but we didn't have time.

"And we haven't seen any wolves or brown bears," I complained. "Apart from the human *bjørn* in the velvet trousers, that is."

"No, and it might have been less traumatic to be eaten by a bear than by those frightful mosquitoes," Alicia moaned, scratching at one of the evil red lumps that disfigured her delicate complexion. "I wish I'd bought a bigger bottle of that anti-mosquito oil."

Our last activity at Karasjok was a late-night trip in

a Lapp boat on a trout-infested river. The boat, like a long, wide canoe, would normally have been propelled by poles, but ours was fitted with a motor. Alicia and I sat on skins on the floor of the boat and trailed our hands in the water, where the trout were so near the surface we could easily have "tickled" and whisked them out had we known the knack.

"But how would we cook them? We can't eat them raw," Alicia pointed out.

Our party grouped together afterwards on the river bank, where Edvarda, before saying goodbye, led us in a sentimental rendering of the Norwegian National Anthem. Most of the gathering had tears in their eyes as they sang of their weatherbeaten land with its thousand homes and ancient sagas. To our embarrassment, Edvarda's parting words were an equally sentimental eulogy in praise of the wonderful British, who had fought to release them all from Nazi bondage.

It was time at last for Alicia to say a fond farewell to her paramour, who had driven us so valiantly and negotiated so many hazards, including a herd of reindeer on the road. The pair of them disappeared behind some dwarf birches and reappeared 15 minutes later looking dishevelled.

"And now for North Cape!" I said as we climbed aboard the Sørøy.

To make up for her recent sloth Alicia reluctantly agreed to accompany me up the hundreds of steep steps cut in the 307-metre sheer cliff face of the North Cape plateau.

I assured her it was the only way to get there – a fact we both began to regret as we toiled breathlessly up the narrow zigzag "staircase", passing a party of women from the national union of Norwegian housewives, who were on their way down.

Our efforts were rewarded by the chance to send

picture postcards with North Cape stamps and postmarks from the wooden pavilion at the top. We were also awarded North Cape diplomas – "and we've jolly well earned them", I panted.

The next short stage of our voyage was delayed a couple of hours as the Sørøy broke down and had to be towed to Hammerfest, the most northerly town in Europe, which also claimed the distinction of being the first town in the world to get electric street lighting, in 1890.

"And I should think they needed it, with all that winter darkness," said Alicia.

Hammerfest was one of the many northern towns which had been razed by the Germans in 1945, only the chapel escaping destruction, and we were not impressed by the new architecture. We were glad when it was time to join the coastal steamer for the southbound leg of the trip, and I was determined that this time I would be the one to have the fun.

I didn't have long to wait. We had been on the ship for only 15 minutes and were steaming out from port when a good-looking member of the crew accosted me on deck. It transpired that he was the radio officer and his name was Lars.

"If you come to my cabin this evening I will show you my equipment," he promised.

We were standing immediately outside the cabin Alicia and I were to share, and I was aware that she was just the other side of the open porthole, listening.

"I'd love that," I told my new acquaintance in a loud voice, flaunting my triumph for Alicia's benefit.

For the next few days I learned plenty about the duties and capabilities of a radio officer. Alicia learned patience and the joys of solitary contemplation, for no other likely lads emerged from among the crew or passengers to keep her company. However, she was the one who saw most of the awe-inspiring Arctic landscape as viewed from the sea – the eiderduck, puffins, fantastic shaped islands and spectacular glaciers and waterfalls.

I joined her on deck whenever Lars was on duty and caught the dazzling midnight sun – so bright it hurt our eyes to look at it – framed between the jagged peaks of the Lofoten Islands, which straddled the magical landscape for more than 100 kilometres.

Nor did I miss the picturesque fishing village of Svolvaer, where our ship stopped for 20 minutes. The waterfront was bustling with activity, for only six years ago the fishing industry in the Lofotens had peaked, with a year's catch of 146,000 tons by 20,500 men. Today it was still a thriving port, as we could see from the many racks laden with fish hung up to dry in the sun and wind – evidence of only one aspect of seafaring toil.

As we lingered to watch the trawlermen preparing their craft for the next trip, we were both hotly wooed by two stalwart whalers bent on a last amorous fling before taking to the stormy seas again in pursuit of their hazardous livelihood. One of them grinned at me lasciviously and I shrank back. He had teeth like a Moby Dick and breath to match, and I knew how Jonah must have felt the instant before he was sucked into the belly of the whale. This human mouth was smaller but no less offensive, and I made a hasty getaway after smartly sidestepping to escape his grabbing hands.

I didn't wait to see what had happened to Alicia, but she turned up just in time to rejoin the mail steamer before it chugged out of Svolvaer harbour. I never found out what, if any, pre-whaling experiences she had enjoyed.

Our next excitement was when the ship entered the narrow, steep-sided Trollfjord, where the hooter had to remain silent for fear of starting a landslide. We left the ship, and my handsome radio officer, at the port of

Molde, known as the Town of Roses, which had been largely destroyed in 1940 but still had its glorious views. It could also boast of being the scene of a famous wartime photograph showing King Haakon and Crown Prince Olav under a birch tree on their way north preparatory to fleeing to England from Tromsø on the British cruiser *HMS Devonshire*.

The final stretch of our journey was by train. We reclined in the comfortable seats of the express as it sped along the Romsdal valley, responding languidly to the cheery waves of children and grown-ups in remote homesteads, for whom the whizzing past of the train brought a fleeting break in the monotony of their daily routine.

The scenery was dominated by the majestic Romsdalshorn and other towering peaks. At their feet a cascading river twisted and writhed joyously like a capricious water sprite, but in due course its wild exuberance gave way to a more stately mood as the broad stream flowed serenely between the wide rolling slopes and green fields of Gudbrandsdal, home of the famous brown cheese. Soon it was the turn of these fertile reaches to tire of dignified behaviour and the smooth waters exploded into a torrent, squeezing tempestuously between savage rocks and leaping down foaming waterfalls like a whirling dervish.

By the time we reached Oslo we felt we had been well and truly educated in the charms of Norway's landscape – and its roving-eyed males.

12
The Tooth Fairy

There was great excitement in the Olsen household one day when Sigurd informed everyone that one of his front teeth was loose. We all had a go at tweaking it backwards and forwards to help it come out, but it clung on tenaciously by a corner. Ingrid was all for pinching it out with a tissue, but Sigurd would have none of it.

Fru Olsen was worried that he might choke on the tooth if it came out when he was asleep, so a family pow-wow was held round the kitchen table to decide the best way to be rid of it without sending Sigurd into hysterics.

Alicia, harking back to her own childhood, suggested the time-honoured ploy of jerking the tooth out with a piece of thread. This idea did not appeal in the least to the little boy, but he pricked up his ears when I said it would be far more exciting to tie the thread to the doorknob and slam the door.

"Your tooth will fly out and crash into the wall," I said, crossing my fingers behind my back against this dastardly lie. "It might even cause a dent in the plaster."

Sigurd looked interested as he digested this information.

"All right, then," he said. "You can do it that way. But I want her to do it," he added, pointing at me.

I felt honoured and promised I would do my best to make sure the tooth shot out as fast as a cannonball. We all gathered round in a circle to watch the ceremony and

Sigurd by now was basking in all the attention and looking quite cocky.

"One, two, three!" we all chanted, and I gave the door a hefty push. The tiny little tooth flew out and pinged against the wall. Sigurd ran over to inspect the promised dent.

"Where's the hole, then?" he demanded.

"Sorry, Sigurd," I said. "Your tooth was not quite heavy enough, I'm afraid. But now you can put it under your pillow tonight so that the Tooth Fairy will come, and in the morning you'll find it has changed into a five-øre piece."

I had to explain to the others about the Tooth Fairy; Fru Olsen cottoned on fast and said she was sure there would be a coin under Sigurd's pillow in the morning.

All this talk of teeth reminded me that I, in my early twenties, still had a milk tooth as one of my canines had never come through. They all wanted to see it, and Fru Olsen was quite concerned.

"Why don't you have something done about it?" she said. "Dentists these days are very clever."

I was not too keen, but she told me there was an excellent dentist in the village and insisted that I make an appointment for him to look at my baby tooth and see if he could metamorphose it, hey presto, into an adult.

"He is very kind and gentle," Fru Olsen assured me. "You don't need to be afraid."

As I set off reluctantly for the village a few days later I said to Alicia: "I wish I'd never mentioned my baby tooth. Look where it's going to land me – in the dentist's chair."

"Yes, but you might come back with a super new canine tooth. Think how it will improve your sexy smile!"

"I don't think it will be as easy as that," I said. "It will take ages and cost a bomb."

"I expect the Olsens will pay for it, specially as Fru Olsen is the one who has pushed you into it."

When I arrived at the dentist's I had a surprise. It was the most homely looking surgery I had ever seen, with chintz curtains and bowls of flowers. Instead of the usual antiseptic smell associated with surgeries, the delicate perfume of Blue Grass pervaded the room. I even detected this fragrance on the dentist himself, which seemed decidedly incongruous as he was a lugubrious character with an even more mournful expression than Fru Olsen's. If I had passed him in the street I would have marked him down as an undertaker. Here, in his pale pink tunic with his initials, T. L., embroidered on the breast pocket in yellow and mauve, I didn't know what to make of him.

I swallowed nervously, and to gain time and put off the evil moment when I had to climb into his chair, I asked him what the initials stood for.

"Thor Larsen," he said. "And you don't need to look so frightened, dear. We dentists aren't all monsters as people seem to think."

Despite my qualms and his funereal face I had to admit I had never seen anyone looking less like a monster – and even less like Thor, whose fiery visage had gazed down on me in the thunderbox at the students' hut. But was Thor's hammer perhaps less of a threat than this Thor's drill?

As it turned out, I was to escape the hammer-drill. After careful examination of my silly little tooth, Gentle Thor said it would be perfectly possible to remove it and bring down the second canine – "but it would take a long time and you will have left Norway halfway through the treatment. It will be far better to ask your own dentist to do this work when you return home."

I was so relieved that I leapt out of his chair much lighter of heart than when I had climbed into it and commented on the attractive decor of his surgery. He radiated pleasure and said in a confiding voice: "How nice it is to be appreciated. Most people hate coming here so much they don't even notice the trouble I have taken to make my little surgery welcoming."

Nosy as ever, I was having a good look round. In a glass-fronted cupboard in a corner I spied what looked like ear-rings and brooches, but I thought I must be mistaken.

"What are those things over there in that cupboard?" I asked.

"Ah, you've spotted my hobby," he said. "I make costume jewellery and sell it in aid of charity."

He opened the cupboard and brought out a tray of trinkets to show me. I looked at a brooch and a pair of matching ivory coloured ear-rings, thinking at first that they were made of cowrie shells like the ones I had bought in the tiny Channel Island of Herm. On closer inspection I had a shock. They were not shells but perfect milk teeth, which had been transformed into miniature floral shapes and posies and given a new lease of life to grace the ear lobes and lapels of ladies.

The dentist laughed when he saw my expression. "Pretty, aren't they? And look at these necklaces – they are just the same. The village children save their baby teeth for me so that I can use them for my jewellery. I could have had yours, except that it's a bit worn."

He added: "I even make use of the ugly old teeth, too, though. Have a look at these."

I was even more amazed as with a flourish he produced half a dozen maracas and rattled them under my nose.

"What do you think is in these dried gourds? Yes, dear, you're right – some of the teeth I have pulled out, fillings and all."

I went home in a daze. Everyone, including the

workmen, was called into the kitchen to be regaled with an account of my visit to the dentist.

Fru Olsen said: "I have often noticed how cosy his surgery is and thought it odd that he wears a pink tunic, but I never knew about his tooth jewellery."

"Is that what the Tooth Fairy has done with my tooth?" asked Sigurd.

"Yes," said his mother. "Isn't it nice to know that the Tooth Fairy needs all your baby teeth so that they won't be wasted?"

Sigurd didn't answer but he looked thoughtful. We guessed he probably wouldn't make so much fuss when it was time for the next door-slamming tooth extraction.

When he had gone out, Alicia looked at me. "Aren't you the lucky one – it's not everyone who has the chance to see the Tooth Fairy at work."

A week or so after this dental diversion Fru Olsen suddenly announced she had chartered a private seaplane to go and visit her father, who was dangerously ill at his home on the west coast. She said there was no airport in the region and it would take far too long to get there by land and ferry.

While his wife was away Herr Olsen decided to go on an eight-day hunting trip with the four dogs. Before he set off we teased him mercilessly on seeing him stuff a dozen or so rolls of toilet paper into his rucksack.

His eyes twinkled. "Do not scorn the humble toilet roll – it saved my life once in the war."

The Germans, he said, had stopped him to search his rucksack on a country road near Oslo.

"I thought my end had come as I had some resistance leaflets and a secret radio transmitter at the bottom of the pack. I waited with bated breath, but by the time they had pulled out half a dozen rolls of lavatory paper they started to laugh and sent me on my way."

While Herr and Fru Olsen were away we servants

had the house to ourselves apart from the children. By now there was a third housemaid, Jorunn, who had been engaged well in advance of our threatened departure for Italy later in the autumn.

A rumbustious blonde country girl, she introduced us to all sorts of novel delights such as leaping from the rafters of the barn into the hay far below. At first Alicia and I were timid and hesitated to indulge in this hilarious sport – which we later learned was a favourite pastime of the children – but once we had shut our eyes and launched ourselves into space, we became addicted.

Our interest in the hayloft was further stimulated when the plumber, Nils, and Olaf the painter, who had until now been forced to keep their distance owing to Herr Olsen's eagle eye, discovered our infantile carryings-on and gleefully came to join us during their lunch break.

"Funny," said Alicia. "I thought the Norwegians never took a lunch break as they finish work so early."

Snuggled warmly in the hay one lunchtime with Olaf, who was busy picking congealed paint of varying hues from under his fingernails, I heard all about the remote village he came from in the western fjord country.

"We went through your village in the bus," I told him. "Yes, it was beautiful."

He gave me a crushing bear-hug and said: "You wait until we've finished the job here and you can come back with me. I'll show you all you need to know."

"I'm sure you will," I said, thinking to myself: "I won't get very far as a painter's moll."

Until now only one of the workmen restoring the house had made any advances towards us. I was lying in bed one evening gazing drowsily through the window at the forest-clad hills when I became aware that someone was moving slowly along the scaffolding outside the house. I watched curiously, thinking he was taking an easy route down to the garden from the bedroom next door, though I was puzzled that he was wearing only pyjama trousers. When he started tapping eagerly at the window and indicating I should open it I realised he had other sport in mind than mere climbing-frame practice.

The would-be Don Juan was not the painter. He wasn't even the plumber. To my annoyance he was the only workman we hadn't even taken into account as a possible conquest because he was so young – far too young to appeal to either of us.

I jumped out of bed and closed the curtains with a scornful grimace. From that time on we nicknamed my thwarted swain "Lover Boy".

While the Olsens were away, everything ran smoothly until one afternoon when Elsa failed to return home on the school bus. There was panic as Ingrid rang round the possible places where the child might be, but no one had seen her. Three hours passed and she still did not turn up, so Ingrid decided it was time to phone the police.

Twenty minutes later two officers arrived in a smart police car and came into the kitchen to discuss the crisis. One of them was the policeman who had admired my eyes earlier in the year when we registered with him.

"So this is where you are hiding," he said, giving me an even saucier look than on the first occasion. "All we need now is to find where young Elsa is hiding."

A plan of action was drawn up. Ingrid was to go with one of the officers to tour the area by car, leaving Jorunn and Alicia at home in case the child turned up.

"And you and I will go and look for her in the woods," my admirer said. "I understand you can show me her favourite haunts."

Alicia piped up: "I can take you to where she plays – I've often seen where she goes in the woods."

She jostled me aside and prepared to set off with the policeman in my place. Ignoring her, he put his arm round my waist and shepherded me out of the back door and towards the forest. Poor Alicia, I thought, snubbed and relegated to the servants' quarters. I just had time to turn and revel in her look of fury as she flounced out of the room.

"Now," said the policeman, "where are we to look?"

I told him Elsa had a secret hideout a mile or so from the house.

"It's a sort of cave in the rocks. She says she meets the trolls there and sometimes sees them dancing. She doesn't know I know about it – I only saw her there by chance one day from a distance."

"And what were you doing roaming in the woods all alone? Or weren't you alone, you naughty little minx?" he added teasingly.

Minx indeed! "I was picking raspberries for *aftens*," I replied with great dignity. After all, I didn't want this respectable officer of the law to think I frequented the woods for loose or nefarious purposes.

By now we had penetrated to the depths of the forest. The path was rough and overgrown, and when I stumbled – which was more often than strictly necessary – he caught hold of me in a flash to keep me from falling into the bushes.

Suddenly there was Elsa's cave – a dark, dank cleft between massive granite outcrops. Elsa was not there, nor were the trolls.

"So this has been a wasted trip," I said.

"Perhaps not quite wasted," said my companion. "Let us sit and rest for a while. You can pick us a few raspberries to refresh us before we go back."

We sat outside the cave and ate the luscious berries, peering into the murky hole half hoping to catch a glimpse of either the ugly little trolls or the pretty little girl.

I snuggled up to the policeman, at his suggestion, to keep warm and we had time for a quick cuddle before setting off to continue the hunt for Elsa.

"Perhaps we can walk in the woods again soon – we'll have more time then to track down the trolls," he said. "But we'll have to go further into the forest. I would like that."

I assured him I would like it, too, and hand in hand we hurried home, buoyed up by the promise of future troll hunts.

Elsa was back at the house, having been spotted by Ingrid from the police car.

"She was playing in a field with a friend," said Ingrid. "She didn't seem to care at all when I said we'd had the police searching for her. A good hiding is what she needs."

We were all so relieved that she was back safe and sound that she escaped the hiding, but she was despatched to bed in disgrace and told never to frighten us all like that again.

Alicia drew the short straw once again when another emergency arose while the Olsens were away.

We were in the kitchen preparing *middag* when I noticed a drip coming through the ceiling. It plopped on to Sigurd's plate of fish pudding and was followed by another. The drips were soon coming thick and fast until Sigurd's meal was in a pool of liquid.

"With a bit of luck that shapeless fish dish will start pining for the fjords and reconstitute itself into something more recognisable when it finds itself swimming," said Alicia, eyeing the white mess with distaste.

Jorunn, meanwhile, had gone upstairs to reconnoitr and trace the origin of the drips. A few moments late we heard her footsteps on the stairs and she came running into the kitchen, shouting that Alicia's bedroom, which was immediately above us, was awash. At the same instant part of the ceiling collapsed, scattering clouds of dust and plaster all over the meal table.

We all froze in horror. Then down-to-earth Ingrid said: "There's no need to panic – the workmen are around, luckily. Go and fetch one of them, Jorunn, while we three sweep up here."

The water was now pouring through the hole in the ceiling, drenching us as we did our best to clear away the debris. Just as we were getting frantic over our losing battle, because none of us knew where the mains stopcock was, Nils the plumber burst into the kitchen carrying a large tin tub to catch the water.

"Thank God you've come, Nils," said a tearful Alicia. "My bedroom is a foot deep in water. I don't know where I'm going to sleep tonight."

The plumber comforted her. "No need to worry about that now, love – we'll find somewhere for you to bed down later when I've sorted this out."

His first action was to rush down to the basement to turn off the mains, and the flood dried up once the surplus water had run down from the bedroom floor. Then he was off upstairs and the four of us trailed after him, hoping to see him perform an instant miracle.

"Dear me, it's not usually as messy as this in here," he said as he surveyed the sorry scene in Alicia's bedroom. "The leak doesn't originate in here. There must be a burst pipe somewhere in the eaves. We'll have to have a good look, and it's going to take some time."

Alicia was sitting on her bed, which had escaped the wetting, and was drying her feet on her duvet cover. But she wasn't left in peace for long. Nils, it appeared, fancied her as his plumber's mate.

"Come on, my love, don't just sit there moping. I'll fetch you a spare pair of my overalls and you can give me a hand tracing the leak. I need someone slim and supple to crawl into the tight corners."

I could see that Alicia's favourable opinion of Nils was not enhanced by his determination to enlist her aid.

"What a nerve!" she said while he was out of the room. "Why should I be the one to have this bit of work experience foisted on me? I never visualised a career in plumbing."

"It's your own fault," I pointed out. "You've been happy enough to be his plumber's mate in the good times. Now you have to pay the price. Hard luck!"

Even harder luck, I thought, when Nils returned with a pair of his old dungarees and made Alicia put them on.

"They are a bit big for you, my sweet, but at least they will keep your nice clothes clean," he said.

"A bit big" was the understatement of the year. Nils was a large, chubby chap and his overalls swamped my friend. I rolled up the legs for her, which were dragging on the wet floor, and lent her a few safety pins to shorten the straps, and then it was time for her to show what stern stuff she was made of.

"Just think, new horizons are opening up for you," I said, trying to keep a straight face as I hustled her into the eaves. "And I hope you'll have more job satisfaction in your new career than I had as a newspaper reporter."

It was two hours before Alicia emerged from the eaves, festooned in cobwebs. I didn't think she had been of much use to the plumber as she failed to locate the burst pipe. Not that this mattered much as Nils himself had traced the leak in her bedroom after all.

"But I'm very grateful to you, my love," he told her in a smarmy voice. "And as your room is ruined I'll find you somewhere nice and cosy for tonight and come and tuck you in myself."

Thinking back on it, I realised his entire handling of

the crisis was fishy as he must have known all along that the leak had started in her room.

"So all that nonsense sending you into the unknown in his dungarees was just a blind," I said to Alicia. "He was obviously having a bit of a joke at your expense."

Alicia was so cross that she refused to speak to him that night and slept instead on cushions on my bedroom floor. The silence was punctuated by her groans as she tried to get comfortable.

"It wasn't only the hard floor," she told me next morning. "I'm all aches and pains after negotiating those frowsy corners in the eaves. I'm not cut out to be a contortionist."

Our next excitement was early in October, when we were invited by the estate manager and some of the workmen to go with them to a "do" in the village, advertised on local posters as "The Red Bus".

"It's a dance," they said. "It will be fun and you can come with us in our car."

Ingrid and Jorunn decided to come along, too, and we all set off in carefree mood and party clothes. "The Red Bus" was taking place in the village hall, and a high-spirited crowd had swarmed in and were seated in rows of chairs.

"Funny sort of dance," I said to Alicia, puzzled. "Do they do it sitting down?"

We soon found out the reason for the chairs. On to the platform at the end of the hall trooped a gaggle of po-faced officials, some wearing brown shirts and one carrying a microphone. Seeing our bewildered expressions, someone whispered to us that the "entertainment" was a pre-election meeting organised by the Socialist party. An old lady wagged a finger at us sternly and told us to "shut up and listen".

We shut up and listened – for three hours. After a boring political speech by the Labour candidate, which we didn't understand, there were light-hearted and not-so-light-hearted presentations, jokes and sketches followed by rousing songs and three hearty cheers.

What seemed like hours later there was indeed dancing, to thin music provided by one of the team on a mouth organ, but by that time we were all too tired and dispirited to join in. We drove straight home instead.

"The things we do for Norway," Alicia lamented as we were cleaning our teeth in the bathroom. "And we don't even get the vote."

For the Labour candidate, though, the "party" did the party political trick, for he won a seat in the Storting in the general election in early October. The Socialists were returned to power, as they had been every time since the end of the war, so we assumed similar "Red Buses" had been noisily revving up in all the village halls of Norway.

We had now been working for the Olsens for nearly eight months and as far as we knew were the only English people in the village. It was quite by chance that we found we were wrong. Returning by bus from Oslo one afternoon, we were mulling over our day's doings when a young man at the back of the bus moved forward and introduced himself. He, too, was English, living in the same village and working in Oslo for a well-known international firm of electrical appliance manufacturers.

He invited us to tea then and there, and we all enjoyed a good gossip without having to worry about whether we had remembered the right gender for a word or were using the wrong "tone". The three of us marvelled that no one, not even the benign bus driver, who knew us all well, had mentioned that we had compatriots living in the same small community. We met our new English friend only twice more as our spell as Norwegian housemaids was soon to end.

We had one more surprise in store for us before we

set off on our travels. Alicia received a letter from home saying her mother and aunt were coming to see her at the end of the week and would be arriving at Oslo railway station at seven o'clock in the morning. There was no bus early enough to get us to Oslo at that hour so we had to go by taxi, leaving the house soon after 5.30am.

Bleary-eyed and still yawning, we greeted Alicia's visitors and accompanied them to their hotel in the centre of Oslo before joining them for breakfast in the restaurant. It was one of the city's most modern hotels, and when we heard that the rooms cost 15 kroner (75p) a day we suggested looking for a more moderately priced place. We were thankful, though, that our suggestion was not taken up, as the hotel breakfast was a sumptuous affair which made up for our sacrifice in getting up at the crack of dawn.

Our pleasure in the meal was enhanced by the fact that Alicia's elderly guests paid for us, as they did on a number of subsequent occasions when they realised how precarious was our financial situation. Their final gesture of goodwill was to hand over all their toiletries and consumable goods before leaving Norway.

Fru Olsen sportingly gave us extra free time during the visit and even devoted an afternoon herself to driving us all to several beauty spots. On the days when we could not be with them Alicia's mother and aunt made the most of the warm autumn sunshine, pottering about in the shops, visiting the places of interest and taking a trip on the fjord in a motor launch to one of the small islands.

In the evening they sat beneath the avenue of trees where Alicia and I were accosted earlier in the year by the Casanova of the broadcasting centre. And middle-aged though they were they, too, found themselves attracting admiring glances from elderly gentlemen who were sauntering past.

One inebriated suitor tottered up to Alicia's aunt, kissed her on the cheek, offered her a small posy of wild flowers, and started to serenade her off-key and in words of dubious propriety. She blushed, and her confusion knew no bounds when he pressed her to join him for a walk in the park behind the royal palace, but she was spared the ordeal when the ageing Romeo's wife came up behind him, grabbed him and his posy and dragged him away, scolding him in a high-pitched voice.

"If that's the way people carry on in Oslo it's just as well you're leaving soon," said Alicia's mother disapprovingly. Alicia's aunt said she thought it was rather charming and perhaps she'd come back to Oslo one day – on her own.

13
Feathered Friend

The time came, at the end of October, for us to set off on our next adventure so that we could be back home in England by Christmas. We told Herr Olsen we were planning to hitch-hike to Italy, but he did not like this idea at all. Hitch-hiking among the respectable Norwegians was one thing – but gallivanting footloose and fancy-free at the mercy of all those hot-blooded Italians was not be be countenanced.

"Little does he know what his own countrymen are like," I said. "The Norwegians may look pale and cool but they're pretty hot-blooded, I'd say."

With another amazing burst of generosity, Herr Olsen decreed that our return to England should be either via India, or the Panama Canal and California, or the Mediterranean – on a Norwegian cargo ship. All we had to do was state our preference and he would make the arrangements and, of course, foot the bill.

After long heart-searching and frequent mind-changing we eventually chose the six-week cruise to Spain, Portugal, Morocco and Italy, which was to cost him £150. Herr Olsen told us we would need vaccination certificates, adding wickedly: "It will be very painful, you know. You will probably be dreadfully ill afterwards."

His dire warning had no effect on Alicia, but I, the ideal subject for a witch doctor's sorcery, went white – and Herr Olsen noticed.

He laid on the pressure. "Yes, it is almost worse than

having the smallpox. But there's no avoiding it, I'm afraid."

After that I could think of little else while waiting for our appointment with the doctor. At least twice a day Herr Olsen marked me down for a couple more gruesome titbits about his friend who had suffered the "worse than smallpox" fate. Finally the dreaded day came for us to make the expedition to the nearest surgery at a village five miles away, the far side of a lake.

We were trudging along our second mile when an empty bus came along. We hailed it half-heartedly as we had been told there was no service on that route, and to our surprise it slowed down.

"Sorry, but this is not a public bus," said the handsome young driver. Then, encouraged by an equally lusty off-duty colleague, he relented. "But you can come all the same because you are so pretty."

We smiled and boarded the bus. Half an hour later it set off again and we arrived at the surgery, 10 minutes late.

The doctor – the same who had treated me for scarlet fever – wagged a stern finger at us. "You're late. Your appointment was at 2.30."

This was the first occasion I had ever known a Norwegian to worry about time.

"I'm sorry, doctor, we got held up," I explained. "The journey took us longer than we expected."

"All right, then. Get your legs ready."

Alicia's eyebrows shot up into her hair. "For the vaccination – I'll do it on your thighs," the doctor said briskly.

Only now did the full shock of the situation hit me again. Our merry-making on the bus had banished Herr Olsen's horror stories from my mind, but suddenly they came flooding back.

"You first, Alicia," I whimpered.

"Certainly."

She delicately raised her skirt to reveal a shapely thigh and the doctor did the vaccination.

"Now you," he said sourly.

I could swear he had an evil glint in his eye and was going to scratch me extra deep. I suspected that Alicia must have had only a token "do" because she did not even flinch. I squirmed in my chair, nervously bared my thigh, shut my eyes tight and gritted my teeth. To my surprise the vaccination didn't hurt at all. I made up my mind to get back at Herr Olsen for the week of misery he had caused me and bitterly regretted having already tricked him with the "Have a fag, hag" deception as it would have come in handy now.

I was waiting for the vaccine to dry when things went swimmy . . . Next thing I knew I was sitting on the floor clinging to the doctor's leg. He wasn't impressed and inquired crisply: "Do you often do that?"

"I've never fainted in my life before," I said wanly.

I noticed Alicia glaring at me. She obviously thought I had planned the whole thing to get one up on her.

"Don't be ridiculous," I told her later. "I pride myself on my high moral scruples. Anyway, it's all Herr Olsen's fault."

Herr Olsen was delighted to hear of the episode. "Yes, that obviously means you'll have a bad time when the vaccination 'takes' in about 10 days. You should have a high fever and feel quite ill."

Alicia was unsympathetic. "Serves you right, laying it on for the doctor like that."

I didn't bother to answer as I felt too frail, in anticipation. Herr Olsen watched me like a hawk for the first signs of fever, and I coddled myself for the next few days and left the rough household chores to Alicia. She was not amused, especially as my threatened fever didn't develop.

We still had a few things to see to before our departure. During our time in Oslo we had developed an eagle eye not only for the large strapping Vikings but also for the tiny twinkling coins the Norwegians were so adept at dropping. Meandering along the streets, we automatically kept our gaze fixed to the ground while at the same time keeping a corner of our eyes reserved for passers-by – a feat of ocular dexterity which we perfected early on.

The dropped coins afforded only minor treasure, but this extra pocket money enabled us to enjoy a cream cake with our coffee or an occasional bar of not very tasty chocolate. It would be far-fetched to say the streets of Oslo were paved with gold, but Alicia and I made sure we did not miss any of the silver offerings scattered here and there by the thoughtfully laid-back inhabitants.

As our housemaidenly careers drew towards a close we were more than ever glad of each day's "bag" of small change. And when, just before our departure, we took our surplus money into a bank to convert it into Spanish pesetas it netted us just enough to pay for a few picture postcards at our first port of call in the Mediterranean.

I kept one insignificant little coin – a Norwegian five-øre – for sentimental reasons. It was the coin we had tossed on the deck of the cargo ship so many months ago and which had won me the captain.

Before leaving Norway I had an important purchase to make, for I had decided early on to treat myself to a duvet. Alicia came with me to a large store to see what they had to offer, and we were cordially greeted in the bedding department by a spotty young salesman with enormous spectacles. An earnest discussion ensued on the tog ratings of the various types of quilt, and the young man had just offered to help me make my choice by demonstrating the cosiness of the duvets when his boss materialised as suddenly as a genie out of a magic bottle. He shooed the spotty youth away, saying: "Off you go! I will attend to this young lady. She needs someone with my experience to get the true feel of our wonderful bedding. You come with me, my dear, and I'll soon fix you up."

By this time a third salesman had appeared and was trying to muscle in on the duvet demonstration.

"Leave this to me, sir," he said importantly. "There are surely more pressing things for you to see to?"

"Nonsense," snapped big boss as he took me firmly by the arm and ushered me into the stockroom, leaving his juniors to squabble over who should persuade a reluctant Alicia to buy a duvet. I knew their efforts would be in vain as she had no money left.

My handsome escort surveyed the chaos in the cluttered stockroom. "Let's see where we can relax."

His eye lit on a large, shallow cardboard box which was half filled with feathers – the debris from a burst duvet, by the looks.

"Here's a cosy little nest, my dear," he said. "You get in and we'll try out a few togs."

The nest looked as though it had been occupied by another bird on a previous tog session, but I dutifully got in and waited to test a selection of duvets with fillings ranging from duck feathers to pure white goose down. Only eiderdown was not included – "for even here in Norway this will be far too expensive for you, my dear", he explained. "But I'm sure one of these will suit you. We'll try them out together for warmth."

When we emerged from the stockroom half an hour later Alicia was still under siege from the two young hopefuls. She looked at me in astonishment, for I was covered in feathers.

"Good heavens, you look like a snowman," she exclaimed. "Have you been togged and feathered?"

She added in a whisper while the boss was chastising his juniors for annoying her: "I don't know whether you've learnt anything about togs – but knowing Norwegians, I imagine you've had some expert guidance on snog rating."

"Yes, he was pretty hot stuff, I can tell you. I'd no idea there was so much to learn about togs. It's a pity you've no money left, otherwise you could have a lesson, too."

The boss was back, and by the way he was now eyeing Alicia I judged she might be in line for a lesson after all, despite her lack of funds.

"Now, how about you, my dear?" he said in his suavest tones. "Aren't you tempted by our lovely snug duvets?"

Alicia hesitated – wondering, no doubt, whether to pretend she was genuinely a prospective purchaser. But her honest nature overcame her curiosity to experience the delights of the stockroom.

"I'm afraid not," she said regretfully. "I can't afford one this time."

The boss was undaunted. "Never mind that, sweetheart. You come and try out one or two duvets, just in case you want to buy one next time you come to Norway."

Alicia switched on her most seductive smile as she disappeared with him into the stockroom to grace the feathery nest. While she was learning about snog ratings I made arrangements to have my duvet sent home to England by post.

My last transaction before changing my Norwegian money was to buy an antique, Viking-style dagger which had caught my eye among the clutter of a small second-hand shop in a back street. I was entranced by the knife. Its bone handle was embellished with chased silver and topped with a silver horse's head, and its strong steel blade was encased in an embossed leather sheath ornamented with silver. I had not seen another like it and thought it well worth the 200 kroner (£10) I paid for it.

We left the Olsen household amid great sorrowing when the day came for us to set off on our travels. A grand farewell dinner in our honour was hosted by Herr Olsen at one of Oslo's smartest hotels. We had been there before as Herr Olsen sometimes fetched us direct from the shore to dine out with him and his wife. On such occasions he used to march into the elegant restaurant in his gumboots, but the Norwegian hoteliers were used to that – we had seen people doing some fancy footwork in ski boots at a posh dance club near Holmenkollen.

On this our last night Alicia and I were wearing Levi jeans, a new fashion craze sweeping America, which a friend of ours had sent us. Even in these workaday clothes we outshone Herr Olsen, who was as usual in old plus fours and gumboots.

We feasted on roasted reindeer meat followed by fresh *multer*, which cost the earth, and an exciting selection of liqueurs. After this meal – "it cost him 120 kroner (£6), you know", Alicia whispered to me in awe – we all felt a little more cheerful, though the tears flowed as we said goodbye.

Our pockets were bulging with US dollars and other foreign currency – we were only allowed to take 50 Norwegian kroner out of Norway and £5 sterling into England – as we boarded the overnight train for Bergen. Just as the train was pulling away Fru Olsen remembered she had a farewell gift for us – a silk scarf each – and she managed to pass them to us through the window. Herr Olsen then remembered he had bought us two big boxes of chocolates but had forgotten to bring them along. As he was very fond of chocolates, we were sure he wouldn't be too disconsolate. He had, in any case, already given us a most welcome present – our tickets from Oslo to Bergen, where we were to board the cargo ship.

We arrived next morning in Bergen, the city under the seven hills, where Norway's second university was opened in 1949. Its picturesque old German merchants' buildings (which were severely damaged by fire two years later) lined the waterfront as a reminder that the town was a thriving centre of Hanseatic trade in the Middle Ages, when Bergen's prosperity was built on the export of dried fish from the north.

A stroll round the lanes by the old wharf, where the jutting wooden gables whispered to one another across the narrow gap below, was a unique experience. We soon discovered that Bergen was totally unlike Oslo – or anywhere else – in other ways.

Something was amiss and it didn't take us long to realise what it was.

"No one is looking at us," I said in a peevish voice.

Our egos took a sudden plunge. Then the reason hit us both at the same moment. Most of the inhabitants were dark and did not look at all Nordic, so we were nothing special.

"How peculiar!" said Alicia. "They're not even particularly good-looking."

Conversation with the locals was difficult as we could barely understand their accent, but we managed to discover why they all looked so un-Norwegian and in many cases had German-sounding surnames such as Wie, the letter "w" not occurring in true Norwegian words.

"Bergen has always been a busy cosmopolitan seafaring centre so many of us are of foreign extraction," a trader at the harbourside fish market told us. "We don't say we come from Norway; we tell people we come from Bergen."

As we walked the rainy streets – it was typical Bergen weather – we felt we might as well be in England for all the attention we attracted.

"It's not as relaxed and happy as Oslo, is it?" Alicia commented. "The people look rather grumpy and slightly hostile."

"Yes, that rude comment by the French writer seems to be well deserved," I said.

Before joining the cargo ship we still had time for a trip up the funicular to admire the view and a visit to Grieg's summer house high above the fjord. After that, as we made our way to the dock, Alicia commented wryly: "Well, Bergen has been a dead loss as far as male companionship is concerned. I think our fun and games have come to an end."

The ship was lying alongside with crewmen busying themselves on the deck. The captain was standing on the bridge directing operations with a tyrannical air. He was a masterful, bull-necked man in his forties, and his face and bearing looked familiar.

"Well, I never!" said Alicia. "I think this is where we came in! The fun's about to start after all . . ."

And Finally . . .

Forty years later I returned to the scene of my youthful frolics, my dark tresses streaked with silver but my bright enchantment with Norway and its people untarnished. With me I had brought my daughter Jenny, who was the same age as I was in 1953.

We began our wanderings at the tip of the "tadpole" tail, and it was there I had my first shock. Milling about on the North Cape plateau were hundreds of people, swarming in and out of restaurants or viewing a 3-D presentation, complete with stereo sound, on a vast curved screen. This mega tourist complex, created by blasting out hundreds of tons of rock, also included a tunnel, grotto and 33ft wide window giving a panoramic view of the ocean. A satellite link with the Walt Disney amusement park in Florida was the prize jewel in this glittering crown of commercialism.

To add insult to injury, a huge expanse of the plateau had been transformed into a parking area, where hordes of Germans had set up their homes-on-wheels and fat Americans were jabbering excitedly about "doing little old North Cape" so effortlessly.

So how had they got there? I learned that in 1956, only three years after my last visit, a road had been opened between Honningsvåg and North Cape and the only access was now by car and coach. Gone was the slog – but gone, too, the brooding desolation which used to impart a romantic thrill to all who attained their goal the hard way. An elderly Briton was on the verge of tears and I, too, was appalled. To think that Alicia and I had toiled up all those steps to earn our North Cape diplomas – and now these pampered, fly-by-night sightseers were just "doing" the spot as casually as they might demolish a Cornetto!

As Jenny and I made our leisurely way south I was aware of many more changes, most of them more subtle than the North Cape transformation. Some were for the better, others for the worse.

One happy development was that the Lapps were now officially recognised as one of Norway's two population groups and schools were permitted by law to teach in Samisk. Some northern churches held bilingual services, and daily news bulletins were now issued in Samisk, even in Oslo, where many Lapps had settled.

Traditional Nordic customs had not fared so favourably, and I could not fail to notice how easily Norway had allowed itself to be sucked into the Anglo-American cultural maelstrøm, which was threatening to engulf this proud country's unique identity. People seemed to be obsessed with consumer goods, particularly all things American. The only benefit I could detect was that the unpalatable fare had been supplemented by food more to foreigners' taste, though the Norwegians still avidly gobbled up fish pudding and fishballs.

Drink seemed to have taken an even firmer hold on many Norwegians, and the Saturday night binge was a riotous experience to be shunned by the faint-hearted – especially with the inflated price of a pint of lager. Rumour had it that a taxi driver had offered a British soldier £50 for a litre bottle of whisky which, like all spirits and even wines, was not available off the shelves at the local store. The girls talked of parties and holidays, the men of money, politics and work. Sport and sex were a common and abiding interest, with the ski resorts and rate of illegitimate births expanding side by side.

The North Sea gas and oil boom and the wealth it had engendered had turned the traditional Norwegian lifestyle upside-down in many towns and villages. Industrial pollution, too, much of it emanating from other countries, had laid its evil finger on the wonderful countryside, blighting trees and destroying life in countless of the 400,000 freshwater lakes which in 1953 were teeming with fish. Nor had the fjords escaped – many had been polluted by Norwegian industries – and there was still resentment at the 1988 algae disaster when millions of fish and thousands of seals died as a result of seaweed pollution.

In the Lofoten Islands all was doom and gloom. World opinion had forced the whalers to abandon their traditional way of earning a living, but now they were refusing to toe the line any longer. Everyone was on edge and the controversy was fuelled by foreign threats to boycott Norwegian exports and also the Winter Olympics due to be held the following year in Lillehammer, where enormous preparatory work for the event was in progress. More important, Norway's insistence on flouting the whaling ban was jeopardising its chances of becoming a member of the European Community.

One of the few ways I thought Norway was clinging stubbornly to its heritage was the increasing use of New Norwegian, above all in the western fjords, where I found conversation with the locals more difficult than ever. They understood me but I did not always understand them, partly because of their regional accent and partly because many words were different enough to confuse me, though I worked them out easily enough when I saw them in writing.

The local newspapers carried reports in both languages, which were officially of equal standing, and around a quarter of programmes broadcast on the national network were now in New Norwegian. I found it fascinating to compare the two languages but could not agree that New Norwegian, which had first emerged in the last century, was the more melodious as some people claimed. I could well believe that fierce controversy was still raging over the official policy of amalgamating the two languages, a task which was hampered by an increasing tendency to produce weird hybrid expressions by fusing Norwegian with English or American words.

I was delighted to discover that Norwegians were still as disarmingly crazy as ever in some ways. This was brought home to me when Jenny and I spent a night at the pension where Alicia and I had frolicked in the shower with the Japanese men and endured an influx of locked-out guests through our bedroom window during our hitch-hiking holiday.

Einar, the proprietor, was now bearded and balding but as ebullient as ever. He welcomed me like a long-lost friend, and his welcome was even warmer for my daughter.

While we were enjoying our evening meal in the cosy dining-room, Einar proudly pointed out a row of 16 new light globes, each the size of a football, which had just been installed round the exterior walls of the pension.

Jenny and I thought they looked out of place on such a small building, but we assured Einar we would look down and admire the glittering globes if we ever found ourselves at the top of the Galdhøpiggen.

"Yes, my hotel will be seen from far and wide – and tonight is the big switch-on," he added. "You just watch – the lights will be on in a moment."

He dashed outside and sure enough, a moment later, the outside of the pension was flooded with light.

"They're on!" said Jenny. A few seconds later she announced: "They're off!"

"They're on again," I said. "No, they're off. Now on."

Einar was back at our table, beaming. He asked what we thought of the splendid new lighting.

"I didn't know they were flashing lights," I said. "I think they would have been prettier with different coloured bulbs."

"What?" barked Einar. "Flashing?"

He looked out of the window as we chorused: "On . . . off."

Our host vanished. Five minutes later he reappeared.

"Ha!" he growled. "Guess what that fool of an electrician did? He put the photo-electric cell too close to one of the bulbs so they switched on at dark but switched off again as soon as the light came on. Just wait until he comes in on Monday – I'll give him flashing lights!"

That Norway had succumbed to the pressures of commercialism and the modern way of life was nowhere more evident than in Oslo. Gone was its quiet dignity, though I had to admit that many areas of the town had been much improved. The railway station had been enlarged and modernised, and I was perplexed on searching for the dear old waiting room, where Alicia and I had spent so many intriguing hours, to find it had apparently vanished. Eventually I came to the conclusion that it had been walled up – possibly with some recalcitrant snorers inside. I wondered whether, like those unhappy prisoners who were incarcerated in the Tower of London in days gone by, they had scratched desperate messages on the wall with their yellowed fag ends for future generations to marvel at when the building was opened up to sightseers.

The cafe where the band slid into the ornamental

pond was still there but it looked more like an American-style fast food establishment than an old-fashioned afternoon tea shop. A little way up the road was the genuine article – a real live McDonalds. Inside was a rowdy crowd of Norwegians. They were dressed in a motley assortment of garments, predominantly red and many adorned with Norwegian flags, and I did not need to ask what they were celebrating: they were wild with joy at the surprise success of their football team in routing the English in the world qualifying match that day.

The royal palace still stood guard over Karl Johansgate and now had its second new incumbent since my housemaiding days. King Haakon's grandson Harald had come to the throne on the death of King Olav, with a commoner as his queen. He had married Sonja Haraldsen, who used to work in an Oslo department store, in 1968 and I gathered she was a popular choice. Apart from any other admirable qualities she might possess, she was a proficient skier who had competed incognito in a number of demanding events. What better recommendation in such a sports-mad country?

King Harald V had not been crowned, for the coronation of King Haakon in 1906 was Norway's last. The ceremony had now been replaced by a reception in the Storting, where in 1991 the new king pledged an oath of loyalty to the constitution – on North Norway's Sun Day, January 21.

Another disappointment was awaiting me when I looked for the stop where we used to wait for the bus to take us back home after our days off. The quiet fjordside road had given way to a flyover and gigantic car park, and even finding the Olsens' house by car was a major undertaking. My daughter and I found ourselves on the wrong side of a lake, where the motorway led us. On inquiry I learned that the Olsens were still alive and flourishing, but when we arrived in their village after losing our way several times we went right past the nearby church and the Olsen house because the buildings were now hidden behind trees which had put on 40 years' growth.

Our welcome by the Olsens made up for all the disappointments of Nineties Oslo. Little Sigurd, whom I had tucked as a kicking bundle under my arm to carry to his bath, was now a handsome six-footer the same age as his father had been when Alicia and I were his housemaids. He greeted me like an old friend, though he could not have remembered me except possibly by reputation – and greeted my daughter even more affectionately.

Elsa was a charming wife and mother of three, who welcomed us to her nearby home. She assured me that she had not forgotten the days when we had to catch her at bedtime, but I felt it more likely she was only being polite.

My favourite little Hedvig, dubbed backward by her mother, had turned out to be a high-powered career woman and was in foreign parts on some business mission.

Herr and Fru Olsen were ecstatic about the reunion, although neither had ever replied to my letters over the past four decades – a fact which had not surprised me since Fru Olsen warned Alicia and me before we left Oslo in 1953 that she would never actually get to the point of writing.

I reminded Herr Olsen of the "Have a fag" trick we played on him, and he swore he had used the expression to his guest of honour at the dinner – but I still was not sure if he was pulling my leg. I also quizzed him about something which had puzzled me since my return to Norway – the universal use of the "thou" form among all age groups. The "you" form of address had completely vanished.

"Everyone is calling everyone else 'du' now instead of 'De'," I said. "Even shopkeepers and waiters call me 'du'."

"Yes, there has been a great change over the past 20 years or so," he said. "The formal 'De' has been almost completely dropped except in certain business letters, and some people take it as a mild insult to be addressed as 'Herr'.

"We are now even more egalitarian than we used to be, but I still wouldn't address the king as 'du', though some of the younger generation say they would do so."

An amusing sidelight on this subject concerned the famous Norwegian explorer Nansen, who in 1888 skied over Greenland with another man. Herr Olsen said it was only after the two had suffered hardship and danger together for a year that Nansen suggested they should call each other "du".

I asked how the Norwegians felt about the Germans these days and was told they and the Swedes were still unpopular.

"The English and Danes are still our favourites," he assured me.

While we were reminiscing after a supper of omelette and fruit, Sigurd and Jenny vanished for nearly two hours. On the drive back to Oslo she told me he had shown her over the estate. From her barely concealed excitement, I guessed he had shown her more than mere forests and farm buildings – a suspicion that was strengthened when she said casually: "Sigurd has invited me to come over and stay with them next year."

"I'm sure that will be great fun," I replied, and, knowing Norwegians, I couldn't doubt it. I even harboured a secret whimsical thought that if the two young people fell in love I might end up related, as an in-law, to my former employers.

Our holiday was nearing its end and I still had a

number of things to do before setting off for home. With me I had brought my treasured Viking dagger, which had been my last purchase 40 years ago. Its sharp point now protruded aggressively from the sheath, for the ornamental silver tip of the leather had long since worn loose and been lost. A silversmith in England had been reluctant to tackle the repair and suggested I should take it to be done in Norway as I was going there on holiday.

It did not prove as easy to follow his advice as I anticipated, for while my daughter toured the City Hall I plodded round the town for two hours before I finally tracked down a silversmith in a backstreet workshop. He said he would make a new tip for the sheath and his charge would be 500 kroner (about £45 at the current exchange rate).

I gulped, but agreed to leave the dagger and have it sent to England when the repair was completed. I had been relying on the 500 kroner to see me through to the end of my holiday and resigned myself to going home with only token gifts for the rest of the family.

Wandering back in the direction of the ornamental lake, where I was to meet my daughter, I happened to pass a coin dealer's shop. I paused to glance in the window and spotted a display of old coins which looked very ordinary to me. In my pocket I had a motley assortment of Norwegian copper coins, some dating from the Twenties and long since obsolete. I had intended to take them into a bank and ask for a few modern kroner – if I was lucky – in exchange, but the search for a silversmith had driven other thoughts from my mind.

Plucking up courage to enter the superior-looking coin shop, I approached the superior-looking man who came forward to greet me, no doubt in the expectation of some high-powered transaction. His reaction was not favourable as I spread my handful of coins on the counter. After rummaging through them disparagingly he muttered: "Hmm. I'm afraid none of these is valuable, and some of them are old Swedish coins and quite common."

His eye lit on a dull-looking copper coin which I had unintentionally scooped out of my pocket with the others. It was my precious five-øre which had won me the captain in the toss so many years ago.

After a swift examination of the coin, the dealer said: "I can give you 500 kroner for that one. It is the only coin of any value."

I gasped: "Why, what is it?"

"It's a 1945 five-øre and they are quite rare now," he replied. "Do you want to sell it?"

I hesitated only briefly before agreeing. After all, the toss of the coin was a long time ago and today I needed the money.

My jubilation was tinged with nostalgia as I pushed past the swarms of teenagers milling around in the pedestrian precinct which now aggressively sliced Karl Johansgate in two. One of the city's more recent concessions to the youth and tourist cult, it was a forum for the clusters of jaunty young motorcyclists who held court there beside their powerful machines.

Blaring music spilled out over the pavements from the open doors of the gaudy fashion boutiques, and not far away the noisy crowds jostling around the immigrant street vendors' kiosks imparted a fairground atmosphere to the once-quiet sidewalks near the Storting. Hundreds of self-centred tourists from all corners of the world, each batch isolated in its own little cocoon, had congregated to admire the fountains showering their sparkling droplets into the ornamental lake.

I had already realised that thousands of immigrants, including refugees from Hungary, Vietnam and other Asian countries, now lived and worked in Norway so for the indigenous population the sight of foreigners was no longer the thrill it once was. This fact was brought forcibly home to me as I watched my daughter coming across the grass towards me. Her hair was as dark as mine had been at her age, and she was prettier. Yet no admiring eyes followed her, and the only attention she attracted was a disapproving look from an elderly Indian who narrowly missed colliding with her.

Things are certainly a bit different from the days when Alicia and I used to sit beneath the avenue of trees basking in the warmth of admiring glances, I thought to myself. As I sat beside Jenny dreamily watching the play of the fountains, I became aware that someone on the other side of the water was staring at me. The man's face looked faintly familiar and I was searching my memory to place it when he came up to me and held out his hand.

"You probably won't remember me, but I was sure I recognised you," he said. "You were on a cargo boat I was serving on . . ."

Suddenly it came back to me. This middle-aged man with greying hair was Alicia's friend Carl, third mate and second prize in our mischievous toss. We sat and chatted, and he could not resist flirting a little with my lovely daughter. He asked after Alicia – I told him she was married to a pig farmer and had seven children – and I asked after the captain.

"That domineering old tyrant!" he laughed. "He's still going strong and bossing everyone about in an old people's home on the west coast. There's another friend of yours there, too – the chief engineer. Do you remember him?"

"I certainly do," I replied. "He always had an eye for the girls."

"Not any longer. He has a dicky eyeball and wears an eye patch over it. He tells people he hurt his eye in an explosion in the engine room, but the story is some female took a poke at him when he got too fresh."

When he had gone I penned a postcard to Alicia with the news I had just gleaned of our old sparring partners. After that my daughter and I enjoyed a leisurely evening *middag* at our hotel, where the menu this evening had, sadly, regressed – perhaps to remind me of former fishier days.

As I reflected on my past amorous adventures and today's numismatic success in this bewitching country, even the four odious, odorous, misshapen fishballs, disguised this time as roast potatoes, failed to diminish my pleasure at having financed the repair of my dagger with an old copper coin. I would have been less smug had I been able to foresee the pitfalls that lay ahead before the saga of the Viking dagger could be blessed with a happy ending.

Back in England six months later, I still had no news from the silversmith, and repeated letters were ignored. A visit on my behalf by a Norwegian friend elicited an assurance from the silversmith that the work was completed and the dagger would be in the post the following day. Five weeks later there was still no sign of it. I decided it was time to call in the big guns – so I rang up the British Embassy in Oslo and explained my predicament.

"I'll see what I can do," a member of the staff promised.

A phone call a few days later threw light on the mystery, but brought me no nearer retrieving my property.

"The work has been done but the silversmith can't send the dagger because the Norwegian Post Office says it is classed as an offensive weapon and refuses to accept it," my embassy contact told me. "It's a pity he didn't write and explain."

I thought "pity" was putting it mildly, and the news merely confirmed my suspicion that Norwegians were reluctant to write letters if they could possibly wriggle out of it. It fell to the lady at the embassy to find a solution to the problem, and she came up trumps. She phoned to say the dagger would be winging its way home in the luggage of a Norwegian member of staff who was visiting England. I was to meet her at a fashion show at a big London store, where the hand-over would take place.

Thus this strange cloak-and-dagger episode came to a happy conclusion in true nutty Norwegian style. A week later my cherished Viking dagger, its sheath sporting a gleaming chased silver tip, was safely back in my grasp and I could boast at long last that I had truly had a double win with my lucky five-øre coin.

BLACK CAT COMMUNICATIONS